Guide to Managing Industrial Hazardous Waste

by
Gary F. Lindgren

BUTTERWORTHS
Boston • London
Sydney • Wellington • Durban • Toronto

An Ann Arbor Science Book

Ann Arbor Science is an imprint of Butterworth Publishers

Library of Congress Catalog Card Number 82-48643
ISBN 0-250-40591-1

Published by Butterworth Publishers
10 Tower Office Park
Woburn, MA 01801

Manufactured in the United States of America

Gary F. Lindgren is the Director of Environmental Services for Ulrich Chemical, Inc. He also serves as an adjunct professor for the Indiana University School of Public and Environmental Affairs on a part-time basis. During the period this book was being written, Mr. Lindgren was a hazardous waste facility inspector for the Land Pollution Control Division of the Indiana State Board of Health. Mr. Lindgren received his BS in Environmental Policy from Indiana University. He was then awarded a graduate fellowship for readings in solid waste management. He received his MS in Environmental Policy from Indiana University.

CONTENTS

PREFACE

Industrial waste management has been virtually revolutionized by Subtitle C of the Federal Resource Conservation and Recovery Act (RCRA), Public Law 94-580. Enacted in 1976, RCRA provided the statutory authority for the U.S. Environmental Protection Agency (EPA) to regulate and require the proper management of all wastes defined as hazardous. EPA issued the bulk of the implementing regulations in May 1980. Since then, amendments and additions to these regulations have been published continually in the *Federal Register*. What the EPA did with these regulations was to provide a set of minimum standards for all who are involved in hazardous waste management—the generator, the transporter, and the owner/operator of treatment, storage or disposal (TSD) facilities. These minimum standards apply nationwide, and many states acted to adopt similar standards and to develop state hazardous waste regulatory programs. Such state-level activity is allowed and encouraged by RCRA, and states may have a more stringent set of standards than the U.S. EPA. States that meet federal requirements can receive what is known as "authorization" from the U.S. EPA. This allows the State Board of Health or State EPA to have primary authority to regulate hazardous waste management within its borders. Until such time, however, all those involved in hazardous waste management must satisfy the requirements of both state and federal governments.

Section 1 of this book gives an overview of the hazardous waste manment system and outlines the regulatory definitions of solid and hazardous wastes. The three determinations necessary for potentially regulated manufacturing firms are described. These determinations are:

1. What are the wastes at the facility?
2. Are any of the wastes hazardous, using the regulatory definitions?
3. What are the hazardous waste management activities that occur at the facility?

Section 2 gives an in-depth explanation of the federal regulatory standards applicable to the different categories of hazardous waste generators. Areas where state hazardous waste regulations may differ from federal requirements are pointed out.

Section 3 presents a philosophical basis for a corporate compliance program and then provides guidance and describes the actions and paperwork necessary for such a program.

Section 4 concludes with some very practical information, unavailable in textbooks or regulations. Topics include selecting a disposal site, what to expect during an inspection, insurance options, legal liabilities and examples of "best management practices."

Industrial hazardous waste management is an exciting and challenging endeavor, of great important to the quality of the environment. Those involved in this rapidly developing field should be proud of numerous recent improvements. Even though waste management is a secondary function in a manufacturing facility, a good compliance program fulfills an important function of the firm, and will lessen or eliminate the liabilities and risks that otherwise face an unwitting or unprepared company.

Gary F. Lindgren

ACKNOWLEDGEMENTS

Looking back on the trail of events that led to the writing of this book, I recognize that I have enjoyed the help of many people who have provided guidance, criticism, encouragement, assistance and opportunities. I can name only a few of them here, but want to thank Dick Young, Ann Arbor Science Consulting Editor, for recognizing my potential as an author, and Lee Langlotz and Guinn Doyle for recognizing my capabilities as a facility inspector. I also want to express my deep appreciation to all of the contributing authors—Tim Kelley, John Lindenschmidt, John Kyle, Tom Fitch, Bruce Palin, Steve Wakefield, John Galt, and especially Jack Cornpropst. Jack taught me, as an inexperienced state inspector, all that I could understand about electroplating and industrial waste management. Finally, my wife, Helen, must be recognized for her patience and perseverance with me and the handwritten manuscript.

I also feel I must express my appreciation to the members of the industrial community in Indiana. As a state hazardous waste management official, I have had extensive interaction with many manufacturing firms. Their questions, problems, suggestions, complaints and practices provided the basis for this book.

I am interested in reader comments on the usefulness of the material found in this book, and would appreciate receiving any suggestions for improving it in subsequent editions.

To my lovely wife,
Helen

SECTION 1

BASICS

This section is a simple and straightforward explanation of the determinations necessary to see how a manufacturing firm's waste management activities fit into the hazardous waste management scheme. In essence, the following three determinations must be made:

1. whether the firm generates a potentially regulated solid or liquid waste;
2. whether those wastes are hazardous wastes according to the definitions or standards; and
3. under which regulatory category the firm's hazardous waste activities come.

For some small manufacturing facilities, these determinations have not been made. Other industrial companies played it overly safe and notified for nonhazardous wastes and filled out permit applications for waste management activities not performed at the plant. Ignorance is not bliss when it comes to hazardous waste management. It is important to make these initial determinations correctly, and to document the thinking and information used in arriving at the conclusion.

Chapter 1
INTRODUCTION TO THE HAZARDOUS
WASTE MANAGEMENT SYSTEM

The purpose of this chapter is to give a general description of the overall workings of the federal hazardous waste management (HWM) system. Such an understanding will provide the reader with a framework to better grasp the specifics of the system, as found in the regulations printed in the *Federal Register* and assembled annually in the *Code of Federal Regulations*. The chapter begins with a description of the HWM system and concludes with an explanation of *Federal Register/Code of Federal Regulations* system and other information sources on the regulations.

OVERVIEW

As it was conceived and as it has evolved, the HWM system is a "cradle-to-grave" system. In other words, the regulation of wastes defined as hazardous begins at the point of generation (e.g., a manufacturing facility), covers transportation and continues to the waste's treatment or disposal (e.g., at a landfill). All participants in this system —generators, transporters and owners/operators of treatment, storage or disposal (TSD) facilities—are required to register with the U.S. Environmental Protection Agency (EPA). Each type of participant has a set of regulatory standards to abide by, and only those participants who have registered can perform HWM activities. This registration, known as a notification, is done on EPA form 8700-12 (Figure 1), and notifiers receive a special 12-digit number known as an EPA identification number. Owner/operators of TSD facilities must also submit permit applications for any existing facility engaged in TSD operations. New facilities are not to begin construction or operation without first

3

Figure 1.   EPA form 8700-12: notification of hazardous waste activity.

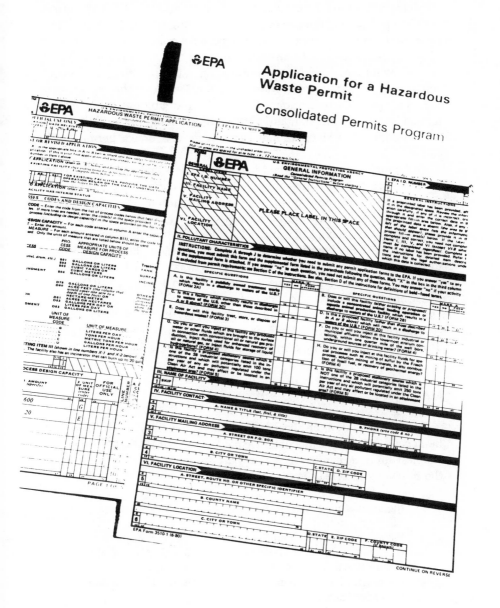

Figure 2.   EPA forms 3510-1 and 3510-3: part A of the federal consolidated permit application.

obtaining a Resource Conservation and Recovery Act (RCRA) permit.

Existing TSD facilities that notified by August 18, 1980, and that submitted the first part of the RCRA permit application by November 19, 1980, qualified for interim status. Interim status is a regulatory concept allowing such facilities to continue operating, pending final disposition of their permit application. By filing Part A of the federal consolidated permit application (Figure 2) and abiding by what are termed "interim status standards," the owner/operator of a TSD facility may continue HWM operations pending review of his permit application.

The significance of EPA identification numbers and interim status for manufacturing firms is that they delimit the facilities that can be used to transport, treat, store or dispose of the hazardous wastes generated by the firm. A generator of hazardous waste can only use the services of a transporter having a valid EPA identification number and must have a valid EPA identification number to offer his hazardous wastes to such a transporter. Further, hazardous wastes can be sent only to facilities under interim status (in addition to having an EPA identification number). This applies to facilities on the generator's property (onsite) as well as commercial (offsite) TSD facilities. There are, of course, certain limited exceptions to some of the above requirements. These exceptions will be discussed in later chapters.

MANIFEST SYSTEM

The transportation of hazardous wastes to offsite TSD facilities is to be accompanied by a document called a manifest (Figure 3). In its simplest form, a manifest is a four-part shipping document containing the following information:

1. the generator's name, address, telephone number and EPA identification number;
2. the name and EPA identification number of the transporter;
3. the name, address and EPA identification number of the TSD facility to which the waste is to be transported;
4. the description and quantity of the wastes and the type and number of containers; and
5. a certification, by the generator, that the wastes are in proper condition for transportation (spaces are provided for signatures from the generator, transporter and owner/operator of the TSD facility).

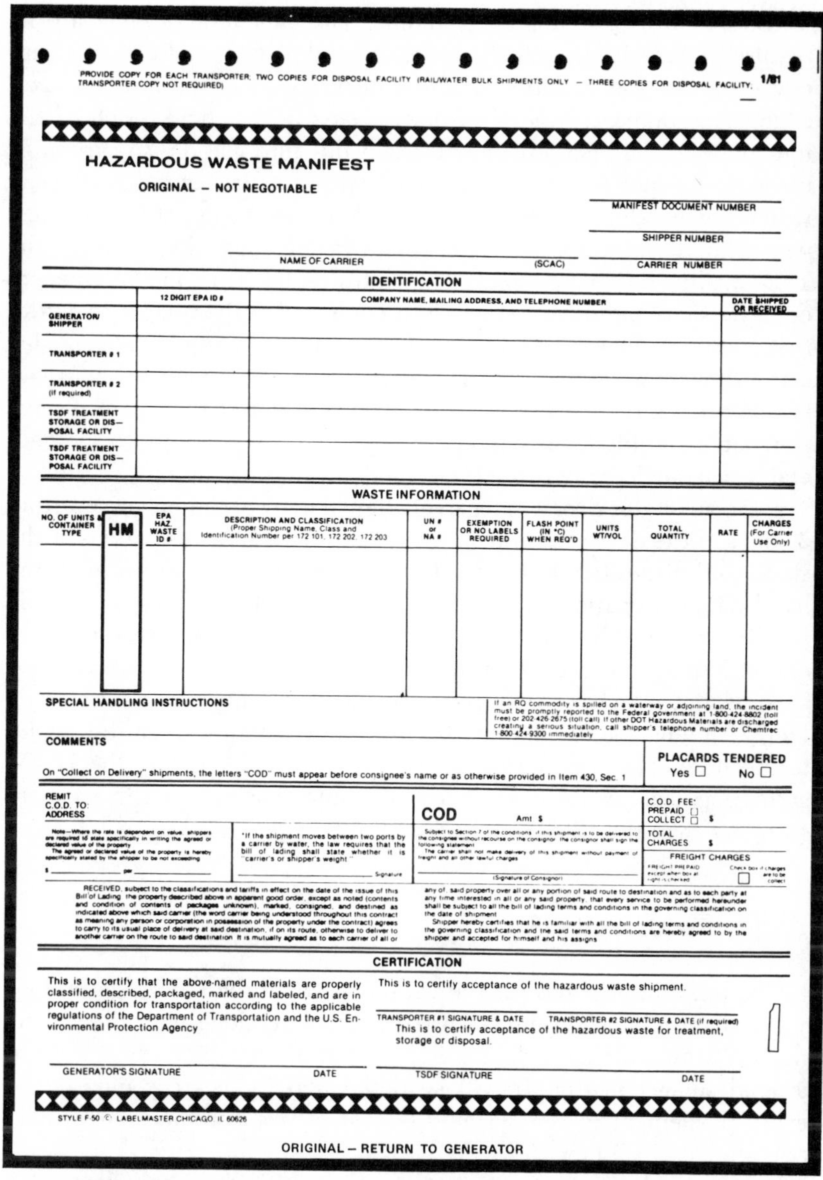

PROVIDE COPY FOR EACH TRANSPORTER: TWO COPIES FOR DISPOSAL FACILITY (RAIL/WATER BULK SHIPMENTS ONLY — THREE COPIES FOR DISPOSAL FACILITY, TRANSPORTER COPY NOT REQUIRED) 1/81

HAZARDOUS WASTE MANIFEST

ORIGINAL — NOT NEGOTIABLE

MANIFEST DOCUMENT NUMBER

SHIPPER NUMBER

NAME OF CARRIER (SCAC) CARRIER NUMBER

IDENTIFICATION

	12 DIGIT EPA ID #	COMPANY NAME, MAILING ADDRESS, AND TELEPHONE NUMBER	DATE SHIPPED OR RECEIVED
GENERATOR/ SHIPPER			
TRANSPORTER # 1			
TRANSPORTER # 2 (if required)			
TSDF TREATMENT STORAGE OR DISPOSAL FACILITY			
TSDF TREATMENT STORAGE OR DISPOSAL FACILITY			

WASTE INFORMATION

NO. OF UNITS & CONTAINER TYPE	HM	EPA HAZ. WASTE ID #	DESCRIPTION AND CLASSIFICATION (Proper Shipping Name, Class and Identification Number per 172.101, 172.202, 172.203	UN # or NA #	EXEMPTION OR NO LABELS REQUIRED	FLASH POINT (IN °C) WHEN REQ'D	UNITS WT/VOL	TOTAL QUANTITY	RATE	CHARGES (For Carrier Use Only)

SPECIAL HANDLING INSTRUCTIONS

If an RQ commodity is spilled on a waterway or adjoining land, the incident must be promptly reported to the Federal government at 1-800-424-8802 (toll free) or 202-426-2675 (toll call). If other DOT Hazardous Materials are discharged creating a serious situation, call shipper's telephone number or Chemtrec 1-800-424-9300 immediately.

COMMENTS

On "Collect on Delivery" shipments, the letters "COD" must appear before consignee's name or as otherwise provided in Item 430, Sec. 1

PLACARDS TENDERED Yes ☐ No ☐

REMIT C.O.D. TO: ADDRESS

COD Amt $

C.O.D. FEE* PREPAID ☐ COLLECT ☐ $

TOTAL CHARGES $

Note—Where the rate is dependent on value, shippers are required to state specifically in writing the agreed or declared value of the property. The agreed or declared value of the property is hereby specifically stated by the shipper to be not exceeding $ ______ per ______

*If the shipment moves between two ports by a carrier by water, the law requires that the bill of lading shall state whether it is "carrier's or shipper's weight." ______ Signature

Subject to Section 7 of the conditions, if this shipment is to be delivered to the consignee without recourse on the consignor, the consignor shall sign the following statement: The carrier shall not make delivery of this shipment without payment of freight and all other lawful charges. ______ (Signature of Consignor)

FREIGHT CHARGES

FREIGHT PREPAID except when box at right is checked. Check box if charges are to be collect ☐

RECEIVED, subject to the classifications and tariffs in effect on the date of the issue of this Bill of Lading, the property described above in apparent good order, except as noted (contents and condition of contents of packages unknown), marked, consigned, and destined as indicated above which said carrier (the word carrier being understood throughout this contract as meaning any person or corporation in possession of the property under the contract) agrees to carry to its usual place of delivery at said destination, if on its route, otherwise to deliver to another carrier on the route to said destination. It is mutually agreed as to each carrier of all or any of, said property over all or any portion of said route to destination and as to each party at any time interested in all or any said property, that every service to be performed hereunder shall be subject to all the bill of lading terms and conditions in the governing classification on the date of shipment.

Shipper hereby certifies that he is familiar with all the bill of lading terms and conditions in the governing classification and the said terms and conditions are hereby agreed to by the shipper and accepted for himself and his assigns.

CERTIFICATION

This is to certify that the above-named materials are properly classified, described, packaged, marked and labeled, and are in proper condition for transportation according to the applicable regulations of the Department of Transportation and the U.S. Environmental Protection Agency.

This is to certify acceptance of the hazardous waste shipment.

TRANSPORTER #1 SIGNATURE & DATE TRANSPORTER #2 SIGNATURE & DATE (if required)

This is to certify acceptance of the hazardous waste for treatment, storage or disposal.

GENERATOR'S SIGNATURE DATE TSDF SIGNATURE DATE

STYLE F-50 © LABELMASTER CHICAGO, IL 60626

ORIGINAL — RETURN TO GENERATOR

Figure 3. Hazardous waste manifest (courtesy Labelmaster).

The purpose of the manifest is to provide a system whereby wastes can be tracked from the point of generation to their delivery to a TSD facility.

The manifest system is fairly simple. The generator supplies all the required information on the manifest and signs the manifest. The generator obtains the signature of the transporter and the date, acknowledging acceptance of the hazardous waste on that date. Each of the four parts of the manifest must contain this information, so carbon or carbonless paper is often used. The transporter leaves a signed copy with the generator and takes the remaining three copies of the manifest with him. The transporter then is required to take the waste to the TSD facility designated on the manifest. The TSD facility owner/operator signs and dates the manifest on arrival of the wastes, to certify that the hazardous waste shipment was received. Any significant discrepancies between the wastes, as received, and the manifest information is to be noted on the manifest. The transporter is then to receive a signed copy; the facility retains a copy and sends a copy to the generator, acknowledging receipt.

If the generator does not receive a signed copy of the manifest within 35 days of the date of shipment, he is to initiate an investigation of the status and disposition of the wastes. If a copy of the manifest with the handwritten signature of the owner/operator of the designated TSD facility is not received within 45 days of the date of shipment, the generator is to file an "exception report" with EPA.

Some states have specific requirements regarding the manifest system, including the use of state forms and submittal of manifest copies to the state. The specifics of the regulations implementing the HWM system, as well as areas where certain states have chosen to be more stringent than the EPA, are discussed in Section 2.

HWM REGULATIONS

The relevant citations for the various parts of the federal hazardous waste management system are listed in Table I, along with the subject matter. Most state hazardous waste regulations are similarly organized around subject matter. It will be noted that there are standards for every participant in the system—generators, transporters and owner/operators of TSD facilities.

These standards, as they relate to the activities of manufacturing firms, will be explained in detail in Section 2. The chapters in Section 2 are organized to correlate with the determinations outlined in Section 1. As a result, the regulatory standards applicable to each regulatory category are in separate chapters.

Table I. Federal HWM System Regulations (40 CFR)

Part	Title and Brief Description	Discussed in Chapter(s)
260	"Hazardous Waste Management System: General"—definitions and delisting petitions	2
261	"Identification and Listing of Hazardous Waste"—definitions of solid waste and hazardous waste; exclusions; requirements for small-quantity generators and hazardous waste that is used, reused, recycled or reclaimed; characteristics of hazardous waste; lists of hazardous wastes	2, 3, 8, 9
262	"Standards Applicable to Generators of Hazardous Waste"—hazardous waste determination; EPA identification numbers; the manifest; pretransport requirements; accumulation requirements; record-keeping and reporting	4, 5, 7, 10, 12
263	"Standards Applicable to Transporters of Hazardous Waste"—EPA identification numbers; compliance with the manifest system; record-keeping; hazardous waste discharges during transportation	
264	"Standards for Owners and Operators of Hazardous Waste Treatment, Storage, and Disposal Facilities"—general status standards that will be used to evaluate Part B permit applications and that will apply to facilities possessing a full RCRA permit	
265	"Interim Status Standards for Owners and Operators of Hazardous Waste Treatment, Storage, and Disposal Facilities"—operating requirements for existing HWM facilities under interim status, until final disposition of their permit application	5, 10, 11
122	"Consolidated Permit Regulations: Permit Requirements"—definitions; basic permit requirements	11
123	"Consolidated Permit Regulations: State Program Requirements"—requirements for state programs to receive authorization to operate in lieu of EPA	
124	"Consolidated Permit Regulations: Procedures for Decisionmaking"—procedures to be followed in making permit decisions	

Federal Register and Code of Federal Regulations

Before delving into the regulations, it is important to note where they are found. All federal regulations, proposed regulations, notices and other documents of general applicability or legal effect are published in the *Federal Register*. Printed every working day, the *Federal Register* serves as a source of information regarding the current activities of all federal agencies. The general and permanent rules of the agencies published in the *Federal Register* during the preceding 12 months are codified annually according to subject matter in the *Code of Federal Regulations* (CFR), thus revising the existing regulations to include the new regulations and amendments to existing regulations. The CFR is divided into 50 titles covering the areas subject to federal regulation. Title 40 of the CFR deals with protection of the environment. Each title is divided into chapters, parts, subparts, and sections; a part consists of a unified body of regulations devoted to a specific subject. Hazardous waste regulations are found in Parts 260–265 of the CFR, and the consolidated permit regulations are found in Parts 122–124.

As referenced here and in other documents, the federal hazardous waste and consolidated permit regulations are (Title) 40 CFR (Parts) 260–265 and 122–124. Sections of each part are referenced by part number and Section number, separated by a period (e.g., 261.3). When referring to individual *Federal Register* issues, the reference is ordered by volume and page number. Volume 1 was published in 1936, so the years 1980, 1981 and 1982 are Volumes 45, 46 and 47, respectively. Occasionally the date of publication is included. An example would be (Volume) 45 FR (Page) 33066, which is the first page of Book 2 of the May 19, 1980, *Federal Register*. For those new to the management of hazardous wastes, May 19, 1980, is a landmark date. On that date, the hazardous waste management regulations (40 CFR 260–265) and the consolidated permit regulations (40 CFR 122–124) were printed in the *Federal Register*. The hazardous waste and consolidated permit regulations were printed separately from other regulations, and the result contained approximately 525 pages. Many copies were distributed by the EPA to the regulated community. Copies of this *Federal Register* still contain the basis of the HWM system, but 40 CFR 260–265 has been amended so much since May 19, 1980, that the *Federal Register* of this date is unreliable as a source of regulatory responsibilities.

To have a complete and up-to-date set of federal regulations, one of several alternatives must be pursued. The most obvious is to obtain the yearly edition of the *Code of Federal Regulations*, Title 40, Parts 100–149 and Parts 190–399, and to subscribe to the *Federal Register*. Both are available from the Superintendent of Documents, U.S. Government Printing Office, Washington, DC 20402. In 1982 the prices of 40 CFR 100–149 and 190–399 were $7.00 each, and a yearly subscription to the *Federal Register* was $300.00. One may also subscribe to one of several services existing for the purpose of providing up-to-date regulatory information. One of the more widely known is the *Environ-mental Reporter,* published by the Bureau of National Affairs, Washington, DC.

There are other, less-expensive options available. Many state chambers of commerce and manufacturers' associations are active in the field of environmental regulation. Summaries of federal and state regulatory activity in HWM may be available from them. In addition, many trade organizations also offer such services and may have waste-related articles of interest in their publications. Further, magazines in the pollution control field also cover the topic of HWM. *Pollution Engineering* and *Waste Age* are two such magazines that publish summaries of *Federal Register* rules, proposed rules and notices. Both magazines are available free to qualified readers.

Certain libraries are designated Government Depository Libraries and will have government publications, including the *Federal Register* and the *Code of Federal Regulations,* available for public viewing. In addition, they may also subscribe to the environmental services mentioned earlier. Check with your city's library or any nearby university or law school library for the availability of the *Federal Register* and CFR, as well as other related publications.

State Regulations

Not to be overlooked, due to their relevance and low cost, are state hazardous waste management regulations. A state hazardous waste regulatory program must have regulations substantially equivalent to the federal regulations, to receive authorization to operate a regulatory program in lieu of EPA. The various states have acted on this requirement by adopting the federal regulations by reference, or by reprinting them in the *State Administrative Code* using appropriate language and format.

As indicated above, a state's regulations may be more strict than the federal regulations, and the more stringent requirement will apply. Further, most state regulations relate to the federal regulations as they existed on a certain date. The impact of this is that amendments published in the *Federal Register* may not apply immediately at the state level, especially if the amendment reduces or eliminates existing requirements. Contact your state hazardous waste management agency for a copy of the state regulations and for information regarding differences between the federal and state program and regulations. If necessary, obtain a copy of the federal regulations that the state regulations reference. Appendix 2 lists such state agencies. Appendix 1 lists all the regional EPA offices.

The remaining chapters in Section 1 will examine the regulatory requirements promulgated in the *Federal Register/Code of Federal Regulations* system. Chapter 2 explains the regulatory definitions of solid and hazardous waste. Chapters 3 and 4 discuss the waste inventory and determinations of each waste's hazardous or nonhazardous nature. Finally, Chapter 5 serves as a guide in determining the regulatory categories potentially applicable to a manufacturing firm.

Chapter 2

REGULATORY DEFINITIONS OF SOLID AND HAZARDOUS WASTE, IDENTIFICATION AND LISTING

Before the determinations that form the remaining chapters of Section 1 can be explained, two parts of the federal regulations must be discussed. First, 40 CFR 260 gives the general provisions and definitions of terms, keywords and phrases applicable to the remaining parts of the regulatory system. In addition, a general procedure to be used in acting on petitions to amend the regulations is given [40 CFR 260.20]. Of most interest to manufacturing firms is the section dealing with petitions to amend Part 261 by excluding a waste produced at a particular facility from the lists in Part 261 [40 CFR 260.22]. This provision will be covered later, but it must be noted that the delisting option is not of practical importance to many manufacturing facilities.

An understanding of the provisions of 40 CFR 261, "Identification and Listing of Hazardous Waste," is crucial to correct determinations of whether a manufacturing facility generates a solid waste, and, if so, whether the solid waste is also a hazardous waste. These determinations are explained in detail in Chapters 3 and 4.

DEFINITIONS

Solid Waste

To be a hazardous waste, a material must first meet the definition of solid waste. If this is not confusing, then consider the fact that a solid waste, according to the definition, need not be solid. A solid waste may be in a liquid, semisolid, or even a contained gaseous physical state.

The definition of solid waste is found at 40 CFR 261.2. A solid waste

13

is said to be "any garbage, refuse, sludge or other waste material which is not excluded under § 261.4(a)."

Before listing the exclusions, the term "other waste material" must be explained. According to an appendix to Part 260, all materials are "either: 1) garbage, refuse, or sludge; 2) solid, liquid, semi-solid, or contained gaseous material; or 3) something else" [45 FR 33077].

Only materials in the first and second categories can possibly be a solid waste. All materials in the first category are solid wastes. Please note that sludge refers only to pollution control residuals (from air, water and wastewater treatment). Materials in the second category are solid wastes if they result from industrial, commercial, mining or agricultural operations, or from community activities from which the material:

> (1) is discarded or is being accumulated, stored, or physically, chemically, or biologically treated prior to being discarded; or
> (2) has served its original intended use and sometimes is discarded; or
> (3) is a manufacturing or mining by-product and sometimes is discarded [40 CFR 261.2(b)].

Materials that meet these conditions are called "other waste material" and are considered solid wastes unless they are one of the five exclusions specified in 261.4(a).

The fact that all sludges (i.e., wastes from wastewater treatment, water supply treatment or air pollution control [40 CFR 260.10]) are solid wastes and that materials that have served their original intended use and are "sometimes" discarded are also solid wastes is important to note and remember during the waste inventory described in Chapter 3. It must be emphasized that a material can be a solid waste, according to the definition, even if it is used, reused, recycled, reclaimed, stored or accumulated for such purposes.

Three more terms used in 261.2 are given a regulatory definition. These terms are "discarded," "disposed of," and "manufacturing or mining by-product." A material is considered discarded

> if it is abandoned (and not used, re-used, reclaimed, or recycled) by being:
>
> > (1) disposed of; or
> > (2) burned or incinerated, except where the material is burned as a fuel for the purpose of recovering useable energy; or
> > (3) physically, chemically, or biologically treated (other than burned or incinerated) in lieu of or prior to being disposed of.

A material is considered disposed of

> if it is discharged, deposited, injected, dumped, spilled, leaked or placed into or on any land or water so that such material or any constituent thereof may enter the environment or be emitted into the air or discharged into ground or surface water.

Finally, a manufacturing or mining by-product is

> a material that is not one of the primary products of a particular manufacturing or mining operation, is a secondary or incidental product of the particular operation and would not be solely and separately manufactured or mined by the particular manufacturing or mining operation. This term does not include an intermediate manufacturing or mining product which results from one of the steps in a manufacturing or mining process and is typically processed through the next step of the process within a short time.

These last three definitions were included to give a feel for the inclusiveness of the definition of solid waste, and to emphasize the broadness of the terms used to make up the definition. Again, this inclusiveness and breadth should be remembered during the waste inventory described in Chapter 2.

Nonsolid Waste

The inclusiveness of the definition of solid waste inevitably led to the need to exclude certain materials. The exclusions mentioned earlier in regard to 261.4(a) are collectively entitled "Materials Which Are Not Solid Wastes." The following materials are not solid wastes for the purpose of Part 261:

> (1) domestic sewage and any mixture of domestic sewage and other wastes that passes through a sewer system to a publicly-owned treatment works for treatment [261.4(a)(1)(ii) and (ii)].
> (2) industrial wastewater discharges that are point source discharges subject to regulation under Section 402 of the Clean Water Act, as amended [261.4(a)(2)].
> (3) irrigation return flows [261.4(a)(3)].
> (4) source, special nuclear or by-product material as defined by the Atomic Energy Act of 1954, as amended [261.4(a)(4)].
> (5) materials subjected to in-situ mining techniques which are not removed from the ground as part of the extraction process [261.4(a)(5)].

Hazardous Waste

When compared to the definition of solid waste, the definition of hazardous waste is a model of clarity. Basically, a solid waste can become a hazardous waste by virtue of:

1. being on one of four lists,
2. being a mixture of a solid waste and a hazardous waste on one of the lists, or
3. exhibiting one of the four characteristics of a hazardous waste.

In addition, any solid waste generated from the treatment, storage or disposal of a hazardous waste is a hazardous waste [261.3(c)(2)]. This includes any sludge, spill residue, ash, emission control dust or leachate.

HAZARDOUS WASTE LISTINGS

As mentioned earlier, there are four "lists" of hazardous wastes. The first two of these lists (261.31 list and 261.32 list) deal with process waste and sludges. The 261.31 list is entitled "Hazardous Waste from Non-specific Sources." These wastes are industrial process wastes resulting from degreasing, solvent usage, electroplating, heat treating and mineral metals recovery. The lists assign a U.S. Environmental Protection Agency (EPA) hazardous waste number to each listing. The 261.31 list is often referred to as the F-list because the hazardous waste number for all listings begins with "F." This number is used in the notification process, on manifests, and in certain record-keeping and reporting requirements. Each listing also has a hazard code, which tells why the waste was listed. The hazard codes used throughout the four lists are:

* I: ignitable waste,
* C: corrosive waste,
* R: reactive waste,
* E: extraction procedure (EP) toxic waste,
* H: acute hazardous waste, and
* T: toxic waste.

The second list is found at Part 261.32 and is entitled "Hazardous Waste From Specific Sources." Like the 261.31 list, each listing has an

EPA hazardous waste number and a hazard code. The 261.32 list is referred to as the K-list, because each of the hazardous waste numbers begins with a "K." This list is organized by industry, unlike the 261.31 list. Thus, a manufacturing firm's operations must match the industry description before the firm's solid waste can be matched correctly against the 261.32 listing description. The industries covered by the 261.32 list are:

1. wood preservation,
2. inorganic pigments,
3. organic chemicals,
4. inorganic chemicals,
5. pesticides,
6. explosives,
7. petroleum refining,
8. iron and steel,
9. primary copper,
10. primary lead,
11. primary zinc,
12. secondary lead,
13. veterinary pharmaceuticals,
14. ink formulation, and
15. coking.

If the operations of a manufacturing facility do not come under one of the above industries, the 261.32 list can be ignored safely.

The second set of lists deals with commercial chemical products or manufacturing chemical intermediates, if and when they are intended to be discarded. There is an "acutely hazardous list" [261.33(e)] and a "toxic list" [261.33(f)]. These lists consist of generic chemical names and have a hazardous waste number and a hazard code. The absence of a printed hazard code following the listed chemical's name indicates it was listed only for acute toxicity (261.33(e) list) or toxicity (261.33 (f) list).

It must be noted that these lists were intended to designate the chemicals themselves as hazardous waste if discarded. These lists do not apply to all wastes that might contain these chemical constituents. The substances listed in the toxic list [261.33(f)] are considered hazardous only if the technical grade of the chemical, or the off-specification variants are to be discarded. For the acutely hazardous list, the listing of each chemical applies not only to the commercial or technical grade of the chemical itself and off-specification species when discarded, but also to unrinsed containers and inner liners exposed to these chemicals, and any residue, contaminated soil or debris associated with a spill of the listed material. In other words, with respect to acutely hazardous chemicals, the wastes associated with production, storage and spillage are acutely hazardous, in addition to the technical grade of the chemical itself, if discarded.

HAZARDOUS WASTE CHARACTERISTICS

Having mentioned the listings of hazardous waste, it is now necessary to cover the characteristics of a hazardous waste. A solid waste not covered by any of the listings may still be a hazardous waste by virtue of possessing any one of the four characteristics. These characteristics are: (1) ignitability, (2) corrosivity, (3) reactivity, and (4) EP toxicity. For characteristics 1, 2 and 4, very specific analytical procedures and decision levels are used. These analytical procedures need to be requested specifically when having work done by a laboratory. Otherwise, the results may be inappropriate for regulatory determinations. Any analytical work performed to determine if a solid waste is "captured" by the characteristics should only be performed by a laboratory with the proper equipment and qualified personnel well versed in these special procedures and protocols. It is also important that the laboratory receive a representative sample to analyze. The regulatory definition of "representative sample" was purposely left very general. The definition of a representative sample is: "a sample of a universe or whole (e.g., a waste pile, lagoon, ground water) which can be expected to exhibit the average properties of the universe or whole" [40 CFR 260.10]. No procedures are specified as mandatory for obtaining representative samples. The generator is expected to meet the performance standard implicit in the definition. The EPA included Appendix I, "Representative Sampling Methods," in Part 261 to provide guidance regarding acceptable methods of obtaining a representative sample. Because no sampling methods are designated mandatory, it would behoove the generator to put some thought into meeting the performance standard. This would include both methods and locations for sampling waste streams. This thought process and conclusions should be documented. In this way, there will be written evidence (in addition to the laboratory results) should there be any question of the validity of a nonhazardous determination for a waste stream.

Ignitability

The characteristic of ignitability is found at 261.21 in the regulations. An ignitable waste will present a fire hazard during routine management. A solid waste is considered ignitable if:

1. It is a liquid and has a flashpoint less than 140°F (60°C) as determined by a Pensky-Martens closed cup tester using American Society for Testing and Materials (ASTM) standard D-93-79 for a test method, or as determined in a Setaflash closed cup tester using the test method specified in ASTM standard D-3278-78. Aqueous solutions with less than 24% alcohol by volume are excluded because they typically do not sustain combustion.
2. "It is not a liquid and is capable, under standard temperature and pressure, of causing fire through friction, absorption of moisture or spontaneous chemical changes and, when ignited, burns so vigorously and persistently that it creates a hazard" [261.21(a)(2)]. This is a vague definition without a testing protocol or decision level. The intent is to "capture" thermally unstable solids likely to cause fire, and it is assumed that generators of such wastes are aware of this property. While the flashpoint test protocol does not apply to nonliquids, some laboratories do report flashpoint determinations for such materials.
3. The solid waste is an ignitable compressed gas or an oxidizer as defined by U.S. Department of Transportation (DOT) regulations.

Wastes meeting any of the above aspects of ignitability and not already listed as a hazardous waste are assigned the EPA hazardous waste number of D001.

Corrosivity

The characteristic of corrosivity is found at 261.22. A corrosive waste is able to deteriorate standard containers or to dissolve toxic components of other wastes. A representative sample of a solid waste is considered corrosive:

1. if it is aqueous (water-based) and has a pH ≤ 2 or ≥ 12.5; or
2. if it is a liquid (nonaqueous) and corrodes SAE 1020 steel at a rate greater than 0.25 in./yr at a temperature of 130°F.

There is no provision for a corrosive solid in the definition. The test methods for both of the above corrosive standards are found in an EPA manual entitled, "Test Methods for the Evaluation of Solid Waste, Physical/Chemical Methods," SW-846. A laboratory testing solid wastes for corrosivity should have a copy of this manual. A solid waste meeting the regulatory standard for corrosivity, and not already listed as a hazardous waste, is assigned the EPA hazardous waste number D002.

Reactivity

The characteristic of reactivity is given in 261.23. A reactive waste has a tendency to become chemically unstable under normal management conditions, react violently when mixed with water, or to generate toxic gases. Like the definition of solid ignitable wastes, the reactivity standard is a descriptive definition without a testing protocol. The intention is to identify and "capture" wastes that are extremely unstable and have a tendency to react violently and explode. Again, generators of reactive wastes are assumed to know that their wastes possess this property and require special handling.

A representative sample of a solid waste is said to exhibit reactivity if it has any of the following properties:

(1) it is normally unstable and readily undergoes violent change without detonating.

(2) it reacts violently with water.

(3) it forms potentially explosive mixtures with water.

(4) when mixed with water, it generates toxic gases, vapors or fumes in a quantity sufficient to present a danger to human health or the environment.

(5) it is a cyanide or sulfide bearing waste which, when exposed to pH conditions between 2 and 12.5, can generate toxic gases, vapors or fumes in a quantity sufficient to present a danger to human health or the environment.

(6) it is capable of detonation or explosive reaction if it is subjected to a strong initiating source or if heated under confinement.

(7) it is readily capable of detonation or explosive decomposition or reaction at standard temperature and pressure.

(8) it is a forbidden explosive as defined in 49 CFR 173.51 or a Class A explosive as defined in 49 CFR 173.53 or a Class B explosive as defined in 49 CFR 173.88 [261.23(a)].

A solid waste possessing any of the above properties is a reactive hazardous waste, and is assigned the EPA hazardous waste number of D003. Again, the waste must not already be listed to be classified properly under D003.

EP Toxicity

The fourth characteristic is EP toxicity. The EP is a special sample preparation step in which the solid waste is exposed to conditions simulating improper land disposal. The EP was designed to identify wastes likely to leach relatively large concentrations of any of the toxic contaminants (heavy metals and pesticides) identified in the National Interim Primary Drinking Water Standards. In essence, the solid waste is mixed with an acidic leaching medium (pH 5.0 ± 0.2) for a period of 24 hr. The liquid extract from this leaching medium is then analyzed for the presence of any of the contaminants listed in Table II. Concentrations equal to or greater than the values in the table cause the waste to be hazardous by virtue of EP toxicity. Liquid wastes that, after filtration, are found to have had less than 0.5% solids by weight are analyzed directly for toxic constituents. The analytic procedures for these and other chemical constituents are specified in Appendix III to Part 261, "Chemical Analysis Test Methods."

Table II. Maximum Concentration of Contaminants for EP Toxicity[a]

EPA Hazardous Waste Number	Contaminant	Maximum Concentration (mg/l)
D004	Arsenic	5.0
D005	Barium	100.0
D006	Cadmium	1.0
D007	Chromium	5.0
D008	Lead	5.0
D009	Mercury	0.2
D010	Selenium	1.0
D011	Silver	5.0
D012	Endrin	0.02
D013	Lindane	0.4
D014	Methoxychlor	10.0
D015	Toxaphene	0.5
D016	2,4-D	10.0
D017	2,4,5-TP (Silvex)	1.0

[a]Source: Table I, 40 CFR 261.

The above description of the EP to prepare a waste for analysis is, of course, a gross simplification. The EP toxicity test procedure is included as Appendix II to Part 261 and is also described in "Test Methods for the Evaluation of Solid Waste." The purpose of the brief description of the EP is to indicate that levels of constituents obtained from the EP extract are not necessarily going to be the same or similar to the levels obtained through an analysis for total metals. The levels should be less. Again, the importance of specifying the proper sample preparation and analytic procedures is evident.

A solid waste not already listed as a hazardous waste, and exhibiting EP toxicity, is assigned EPA hazardous waste number(s) specified in Table II corresponding to the toxic contaminant(s) causing the solid waste to be hazardous.

It is worth noting that the EPA hazardous waste numbers assigned to the characteristics of a hazardous waste, as well as to each listed waste, are important to know due to their use in notification, manifesting, annual reports, and other record-keeping and reporting requirements.

IDENTIFICATION OF HAZARDOUS WASTE

Now that the lists of hazardous wastes and the characteristics of hazardous waste have been discussed, it is appropriate to return to the definition of hazardous waste [261.3] for guidance on when a waste becomes hazardous and when a hazardous waste ceases to be a hazardous waste.

A solid waste not excluded from regulation under 261.4(b) is a hazardous waste if it meets any of the following criteria:

1. It meets the listing description on any of the four lists of hazardous waste and has not been excluded (delisted) from the lists under 260.22.
2. It is a mixture of solid waste and one or more listed hazardous wastes that have not been delisted.
3. It exhibits any one of the four characteristics of a hazardous waste.

A solid waste becomes a hazardous waste when any of the following events occur:

1. for listed wastes, when the waste first meets the listing description;
2. for mixtures of listed and solid wastes, when the listed waste is first added to the solid waste; and

3. in the case of any other waste (including mixtures), when the waste exhibits any one of the four characteristics [261.3(b)].

In general, except for listed process residues and wastewater treatment sludges, the point in time when solid wastes become hazardous is when their intended use has ceased or is no longer possible (the material is spent), and the materials are segregated, accumulated or stored for disposal, reuse or reclamation. Remember, a material first must be a (solid) waste before it can become a hazardous waste. Further, manufacturers can have hazardous wastes in a raw material or product storage tank (tank bottoms) or in a manufacturing process unit that are not subject to regulation until the wastes are removed from the tank or unit [261.4(c)]. This issue is discussed further in Chapter 5.

The provision that solid wastes mixed with listed hazardous waste are considered hazardous wastes has important implications for hazardous waste management. This so-called "mixture rule" [261.4(2)ii] will cause the entire quantity of an otherwise nonhazardous solid waste and a listed hazardous waste to become hazardous waste when mixed. This provides a definite incentive for manufacturing firms to be very diligent in segregating listed hazardous wastes from other wastes, as a cost-containment measure. By segregating, the potential for and feasibility of recycling, reuse or treatment becomes greater. In addition, obtaining approvals from regulatory agencies and waste disposal companies to land-dispose the material may become easier.

The regulatory definition of hazardous waste also specifies when a hazardous waste ceases to be a hazardous waste [261.3(c) and (d)]. Remember that a solid waste can be hazardous by (1) being listed; (2) being a mixture of solid and listed hazardous waste; (3) exhibiting any one of the characteristics of a hazardous waste; and (4) being a waste resulting from the treatment, storage or disposal (TSD) of a hazardous waste. In the case of solid wastes generated from TSD of a characteristic hazardous waste or delisted hazardous wastes, a hazardous waste remains a hazardous waste unless and until the solid waste does not exhibit any of the characteristics of a hazardous waste. For listed hazardous wastes, wastes containing a listed hazardous waste, or wastes derived from a listed hazardous waste, the waste(s) must also have been excluded (delisted) from regulation under the rulemaking procedures of 260.20 and 260.22.

The regulatory preamble states that "as a practical matter . . . any wastes removed from such [TSD] facilities—including spills, discharges or leaks—must be managed as hazardous wastes" [45 FR 33096]. This would, of course, include any treatment or pollution control sludges resulting from treatment facilities.

To conclude this lengthy and rather involved discussion of regulatory definitions of solid and hazardous waste, the list of 261.4(b) exclusions —solid wastes that are not hazardous wastes—must be given. The following solid wastes are not hazardous wastes for the purpose of Part 261:

1. household wastes;
2. solid wastes from agricultural crops and animals returned to the soil as fertilizer;
3. mining overburden returned to the mine site;
4. fly ash waste, bottom ash waste, slag waste and flue gas emission control waste generated primarily from the combustion of coal or other fossil fuels;
5. drilling fluids, produced waters and other wastes associated with the exploration for and production of crude oil, natural gas or geothermal energy.
6. wastes containing chromium in the trivalent state and that fail the characteristic of EP toxicity solely because of chromium or that are listed solely because of chromium [the waste must be generated from an industrial process using trivalent chromium (almost) exclusively, the process must not generate hexavalent chromium and the waste must be managed in nonoxidizing environments; specific examples are given in 261.4(b)(6)(ii)];
7. solid wastes from the extraction, beneficiation and processing of ores and minerals;
8. cement kiln dust waste; and
9. discarded wood or wood products generated by users of arsenical-treated wood or wood products.

For the majority of manufacturing firms, only exclusions 4 and 6 would be of potential interest.

With this understanding of the regulatory definitions, those people assigned waste management duties at a manufacturing facility are now prepared to move on to the determinations necessary for corporate compliance. Determination of all the wastes generated at the facility is discussed in Chapter 3. Determination of which of the solid wastes generated are hazardous is covered in Chapter 4. Finally, the possible regulatory categories for facilities generating wastes are outlined in Chapter 5.

Chapter 3

CONDUCTING A WASTE INVENTORY:
PROCEDURES AND CONSIDERATIONS

Perhaps the most logical place to begin compliance with federal and state hazardous waste management (HWM) requirements is to prepare an "inventory" of waste generated from the facility in question. In this manner, there can be no question as to how many different waste streams there are, and where they come from. Determining how the HWM requirements apply to facility operations becomes simpler.

"BLACK BOX" APPROACH

One approach of particular usefulness in preparing an inventory is to look at the plant operations as a whole. This requires, initially, viewing the entire manufacturing facility as a "black box," with inputs (raw materials, chemicals, water and air) and outputs (finished products, wastewater, waste liquids and waste solids). It is important to keep in mind the regulatory definitions of solid and hazardous wastes when looking at facility inputs and outputs.

For manufacturing firms, the reason for existence is the production of a marketable item. However, in most factories the item to be sold is not the only thing produced. There are also contaminated air, contaminated water, and a variety of solid and liquid waste products. Although these waste materials are only incidental to the manufacture of a marketable item, they still must be handled in a proper and safe manner.

Inputs

In using the "black box" analogy, the search for waste outputs begins with examination of all inputs that could possibly become wastes. To

25

discover all chemicals and materials used in facility operations, an examination can be made of all purchase orders for a period of time, say 12 months. Total quantities, purpose in facility operations, price per unit and usage per unit time should be noted.

From this examination, a list of "suspect" inputs should be compiled. As a general rule, the following types of inputs, if used, should always be on such a list:

1. cleaning agents: acids, alkalis, solvents and organic cleaning solutions;
2. process chemicals;
3. industrial oils: hydraulic oils, cutting oils, coolants, lube oils and quench oils;
4. water treatment chemicals: water softening agents, deoxygenators, biocides and coagulants; and
5. surface finishing agents: rust inhibitors, primers, paints, coatings and all chemicals involved with electroplating.

Remember that commercial chemical products, if discarded, can be hazardous wastes. Even though such chemicals are often sold under a trade name, the manufacturer must determine if such proprietary chemicals consist of chemicals listed under 261.33(e) or (f).

Material Safety Data Sheet

The vendors selling the "suspect" inputs to the facility should be contacted and asked to furnish what is known as a "material safety data sheet." The material safety data sheet, also know as Occupational Safety & Health Administration (OSHA) form 20, provides much useful information. The information on these sheets is compiled by the chemical producers and includes:

1. manufacturer's name, address and emergency telephone number, the chemical's name and synonyms, any trade names and synonyms, and the chemical family and formula;
2. hazardous ingredients present, by chemical name, approximate percentage of each hazardous ingredient and threshold limit value for each hazardous ingredient;
3. physical data on the chemical or mixture of chemicals;
4. fire and explosion hazard data for the chemical or mixture of chemicals;
5. health hazard data;
6. reactivity data;
7. spill or leak procedures;

8. special protection information; and
9. special precautions

The value of such information for the proper management of the chemicals (as products, process chemicals or wastes) is obvious. It is important to note, however, that the information on form OSHA 20 is oriented toward worker safety, as workers are exposed to the concentrated chemical product. The purpose in obtaining the material safety data sheets at this point is to have some preliminary information as to the chemical composition of facility waste streams. Such information is important when deciding whether the chemicals used meet any listing descriptions, and which chemical analyses to perform on each waste stream.

Outputs

Continuing the "black box" examination, the emphasis switches to the outputs. The inputs that leave the factory as products obviously are not of concern here. The inputs not accounted for in production, now known as wastes or residuals, are the focus of attention. Determination of these unwanted outputs is less straightforward than determination of inputs. Examination of any waste hauling records and hazardous materials bills of lading is a start, although they are usually too general for this purpose. Here it is important to actually get on the factory floor and examine the production lines and talk to operating personnel. Detailed examinations of facility processes and operations, again using the "black box" analogy, and interviews with select personnel (equipment operators, maintenance and repair employees, and housekeeping staff) are necessary to prepare a listing of all outputs from each machine and activity at the facility. The information that should be obtained in this regard includes:

1. wastes associated with process startup and shutdown and process changeovers;
2. wastes associated with normal production;
3. wastes associated with equipment cleaning, maintenance or repair;
4. wastes associated with process upsets, including the use of off-specification inputs and production of any off-specification products;
5. wastes associated with inventory (of inputs and outputs), including obsolete and expired chemicals, materials and products; and
6. wastes associated with products not meeting customer specifications (returned goods, goods damaged in transit, etc.).

The information on inputs and outputs gathered allows the development of a crude (nonnumerical) materials balance diagram. This flow diagram correlates the various operations, processes and support activities of the plant with the inputs and outputs discussed above.

This preliminary examination will reveal several areas of concern:

1. The waste streams identified need further classification. The composition and quantity of each waste stream need to be determined. Quantity determinations must be made using historical data or statistically rigorous sampling methods. Startup and shutdown procedures, maintenance activities, and differences in production levels must be taken into account.

2. It is necessary to determine if any of the waste streams are regulated under federal and state HWM schemes. All necessary laboratory analyses should be performed on representative samples using U.S. Environmental Protection Agency (EPA) sampling and analysis protocol.

3. Of the waste streams classified as hazardous, it is necessary to determine whether they are exempt, have been suspended from the original listings, or are excluded from regulation due to use, reuse, recycling or reclamation.

4. Quantities of regulated hazardous wastes must be totaled to determine if the facility falls under the small-quantity exclusion.

5. Federal, state and municipal wastewater and air pollution regulations must be examined to determine whether the facility's air and water effluents are subject to regulation. If so, it must be determined whether those effluents meet the applicable standards, and all necessary permits must be obtained.

6. The amount of wastes per unit of production remains unknown.

7. The effect of process and production variables on waste output remains unknown.

8. The storage practices and final disposition of solid and liquid residuals need to be determined. Is the commercial hauler transporting the wastes to a state-permitted facility or an open dump? Is the disposal facility properly managed and operated (regardless of permit status), so as to insulate the corporation from environmental damage lawsuits against the disposal facility? Are federal and state regulations regarding storage and transportation of hazardous materials and wastes being followed?

INTEGRATED APPROACH

It is obvious that the above concerns must be addressed. However, the complexity of the ever-growing body of environmental regulations and the high cost of compliance (or noncompliance) seem to indicate the advantages of some sort of integrated approach toward residuals management. Such an approach would include a strategy to minimize total short- and long-term costs of complying with all applicable requirements.

An integrated approach to solid and hazardous waste management at manufacturing facilities is the subject of Section 3 of this book. First, the wastes at a manufacturing facility must be uncovered, and determinations made as to each waste's hazardous or nonhazardous status. The facility's regulatory category is then ascertained and the applicable regulations are understood. Only after these preliminary steps are complete can a workable corporate compliance program be implemented. An integrated approach toward residuals management is a desirable element of any corporate compliance program.

Chapter 4

HAZARDOUS WASTE DETERMINATIONS: PROCEDURES AND CONSIDERATIONS

Federal and state hazardous waste management (HWM) regulations require certain actions on the part of waste generators with respect to the nature of their wastes. Those who generate solid wastes are required to determine if their wastes are hazardous. Other considerations come into play once these determinations are made. It is the purpose of this chapter to aid in these determinations.

Chapter 2 dealt with the definitions of solid and hazardous waste, and explained listings and the four characteristics. Chapter 3 outlined the procedures and considerations involved with a waste inventory at a manufacturing facility. This chapter builds on these previous chapters and delves into some related considerations.

IDENTIFICATION OF SOLID WASTE

The first step in any determination of the hazardous waste(s) at a facility is the application of the definition of "solid waste" to the waste streams uncovered during the waste inventory. As mentioned in Chapter 2, solid wastes do not need to be solid (i.e., they can be liquid, semisolid or contained gaseous material, as well as solid). Further, all sludges and materials "sometimes discarded" are solid wastes. Finally, a material can be a solid waste regardless of its intended disposition; in other words, a material can be a solid waste even if it is to be used, reused, recycled or reclaimed.

This broad definition will very likely make wastes, sludges, and materials or manufacturing by-products that are sometimes discarded (all uncovered during the waste inventory) solid wastes, unless they are

31

one of the 261.4(a) exclusions. The exclusions of interest to the majority of manufacturing firms are:

> (1) domestic sewage and any mixture of domestic sewage and other wastes that passes through a sewer system to a publicly-owned treatment works for treatment
> (2) industrial wastewater discharges that are point source discharges subject to regulation under Section 402 of the Clean Water Act, as amended

Determination of whether a material is a solid waste is important because hazardous wastes are a subset of solid wastes; therefore, a material must be a solid waste before it can be a hazardous waste.

IDENTIFICATION OF HAZARDOUS WASTE

Once it is determined that a material is a "solid waste," the next step is to determine whether the material is also a "hazardous waste." As explained in Chapter 2, a solid waste is hazardous if it (1) meets the description of any item on any one of the four lists; (2) is a mixture that contains a listed hazardous waste; or (3) exhibits any one of the four characteristics of a hazardous waste.

Supplemental instructions for generators regarding hazardous waste determinations are given at 40 CFR 262.11. A generator of a solid waste is to first determine whether the waste is excluded from regulation under 261.4. At this point, the generator is to determine if the waste is listed. If the waste is not listed, it should be examined to see if it is "captured" by the characteristics. Remember that process chemicals, if discarded, can be a listed hazardous waste by virtue of the 261.33(e) or (f) lists. In determining if the waste is a characteristic hazardous waste, the generator may either test the waste according to approved methods or apply knowledge of the hazard characteristic of the waste in light of the materials or processes used.

The regulations [40 CFR 262.11] do not require that a generator go to the effort and expense of chemical analysis for wastes thought to possess a characteristic of a hazardous waste. The generator has the option of declaring a waste stream "hazardous." Lack of chemical analyses in determination decisions may prove to be a false economy in the long run. This holds for both listed and characteristic hazardous wastes. The data obtained by chemical analysis can yield valuable information about the process and condition of the equipment. Further, such information is necessary to determine the feasibility of recycling, materials recovery or waste transfer, and the proper treatment or disposal methods. Finally, some waste streams thought hazardous may in fact be nonhazardous, and any declarations of the "nonhazardous" nature of a waste will need documentation.

A few other points merit further discussion:

1. Generators falling under the small-quantity generator exclusion [261.5] are granted an exclusion from 40 CFR 262–265 and 122–124, and notification under Section 3010 of the Resource Conservation and Recovery Act (RCRA). To gain this exclusion, the generator must not generate or accumulate more than 1000 kg of hazardous wastes in any one calendar month. Some states have different (lower) exclusion levels than those found in federal regulations. Also, the generator must comply with 262.11 and must treat or dispose of the waste in an onsite facility, or ensure delivery to an offsite treatment, storage or disposal (TSD) facility within the RCRA system or permitted by the state to manage municipal or industrial solid waste. Different exclusion levels apply to commercial chemicals, containers, liners and spill residues from materials on the acutely hazardous list [261.33(e)]. These levels are found in 261.5(e). Further discussion of the small-quantity generator exclusion can be found in Chapter 5, and the regulatory standards for small-quantity generators can be found in Chapter 8.

2. Hazardous wastes that are beneficially used or reused, or legitimately recycled or reclaimed are either not subject to the regulations, or are subject to the regulations only with respect to their transportation and storage [261.6]. Recycled wastes that are hazardous solely because of a characteristic are not subject to regulation under the federal hazardous waste regulations. Listed hazardous wastes, hazardous waste sludges and mixtures containing listed hazardous wastes that are transported or stored before being used, reused, recycled or reclaimed are subject to regulation only with regard to their transportation or storage. One minor benefit from managing characteristic hazardous wastes by recycling is that such wastes are not included in small-quantity determinations under 261.5 [45 FR 76620]. The exemption applies only to "legitimate" and "beneficial" uses and recycling of hazardous wastes. Once again, some states have more stringent regulations on this matter, including strict interpretations regarding what constitutes beneficial use or legitimate recycling. For example, the state of Indiana requires all recycling operations to have a permit, unless the hazardous wastes generated from the manufacturing process are recycled, recovered or reused at the same site by the generator [IC 13-7-8.5-5(e) and

320 IAC 4-3-7(a)(2)]. Further discussion of this issue can be found in Chapter 5, and the regulatory standards for generators who recycle are covered in Chapter 9.

3. Under 261.3(c), any solid waste generated from TSD of a hazardous waste is a hazardous waste unless it meets the criteria of 261.3(d). These criteria are:

1. The solid waste does not exhibit any of the characteristics of hazardous waste.
2. In the case of a listed waste, a waste containing a listed waste or a waste derived from a listed waste, it must also have been excluded from 261.3(c) under 260.20 and 260.22.

Therefore, the treatment residues of any listed hazardous waste must also be managed as hazardous, unless they are delisted and are not "captured" by the characteristics.

4. Procedures for delisting are specified at 260.20 and 260.22. Petitions to amend Part 261 to exclude a waste produced at a particular facility are allowed at 260.22, and 260.20 gives the general requirements for all petitions. These petitions are for the purpose of excluding a waste at a particular generating facility from the lists in Part 261. Any exclusion granted only applies to the particular waste generated at the facility and will not apply to similar wastes from any other facility.

5. The final point to be discussed, but certainly not the least important, is that of the disposition of wastes determined to be nonhazardous. It must be realized that wastes not falling under the RCRA definition of hazardous wastes are still regulated materials. Nonhazardous industrial wastes can still pose a threat to the environment if mismanaged. In other words, nonhazardous status for a waste stream does not relieve the generator of responsibility for proper management. Regulatory standards for the management of nonhazardous industrial waste are discussed in Chapter 6.

SUMMARY

The definition of solid waste, the four lists of hazardous wastes and the four characteristics of hazardous wastes are to be used by generators to determine if their solid wastes are hazardous. Wastes that meet the listing description of any of the lists are automatically hazardous. The generator has the responsibility for identifying a waste that is hazardous by virtue of possessing a characteristic of a hazardous waste. The generator can do so by testing the waste and/or by applying his knowledge of the hazard characteristics of the waste.

Chapter 5 concludes Section 1 by describing regulatory categories under which manufacturing facilities most commonly fall. The waste management activities of many manufacturing facilities can be described by more than one category. The regulatory standards for each category are described in Section 2.

Chapter 5

DETERMINING THE FIRM'S HAZARDOUS WASTE MANAGEMENT ACTIVITIES

Once an inventory of the wastes produced at the manufacturing facility is conducted, and the wastes have been determined to be either hazardous or nonhazardous, the next step necessary for compliance is to determine how the firm's waste management activities fit into the regulatory categories. There are several categories, and, of course, some facilities will fall into more than one. These categories are:

1. solid waste/nonhazardous industrial waste generator;
2. generator;
3. small-quantity generator;
4. generators who recycle hazardous wastes;
5. generators who accumulate hazardous wastes onsite less than 90 days without a permit;
6. generators who store hazardous wastes onsite under interim status pending disposition of their permit application;
7. generators who ship wastes offsite for treatment, storage or disposal (TSD);
8. generators who treat hazardous waste by an exempted method;
9. generators who treat hazardous wastes onsite under interim status; and
10. generators who dispose of hazardous wastes onsite under interim status

This book does not cover treatment or disposal operations of manufacturing facilities falling into categories 9 or 10, nor does it cover storage of hazardous wastes in surface impoundments or waste piles. Inclusion of such operations would complicate matters unnecessarily, since most small- and medium-size manufacturing firms fall into categories 1–8. This chapter provides guidance in the determination of which category or group of categories best match the waste management activities of the manufacturing facility. Section 2 of this book covers the regulatory standards for categories 1–8 in separate chapters.

SOLID WASTE/NONHAZARDOUS INDUSTRIAL WASTE GENERATOR

If, after an extensive examination of the process wastes, pollution control residuals and commercial chemical products sometimes discarded, it is determined that none of the solid wastes produced at the facility are hazardous [or that the wastes fall under 261.4(a) or (b) exclusions], the regulations issued under Subtitle C of the Resource Conservation and Recovery Act (RCRA) do not apply. More likely is the finding that many of the solid wastes generated are not hazardous. It is important to note the existence of state requirements for proper management of solid and nonhazardous industrial wastes, including requirements for any onsite management of such wastes. These requirements will be discussed in Chapter 6.

It is also important to document the data and logic used in the determinations regarding each nonhazardous solid waste. The material safety data sheets obtained from vendors and the laboratory analyses performed on representative samples of each waste provide important evidence in the documentation. A short narrative to accompany these documents should be prepared for each waste stream. Such a narrative would, if applicable, explain why the waste is not a solid waste. If the material is a solid waste, the narrative would state (1) that the waste meets one of the 261.4(b) exemptions, if applicable; (2) the waste does not meet any of the listings of process wastes under 261.31 and 261.32, and that the waste does not meet the 261.33(e) or (f) commercial chemical product listings; and (3) why the waste does not fall under any of the four characteristics.

This is not an onerous task, and will provide ready documentation should there be any question on the part of federal or state hazardous waste inspectors, landfill operators, insurance companies, local civil defense or fire departments, or corporate management.

Remember, however, that the facility's status as a nonhazardous industrial waste generator is not static or permanent. Any one of the following events could alter the facility's status, and should be investigated as necessary for waste management impacts:

1. a change in production processes or waste treatment operations;
2. trial use or change in process chemicals;

3. spills, leaks or process upsets of listed commercial products not normally discarded, or of process chemicals normally nonhazardous;

4. infrequent cleaning, maintenance or construction/demolition operations (e.g., cleaning of product storage tanks, boilers, pollution control equipment and flues; or removal of production equipment, chemical pipelines, or contaminated concrete or soil); and

5. discovery of obsolete, off-specification or expired process chemicals not on the 261.33(e) or (f) lists.

Should any of these events cause generation of a hazardous waste, the facility waste management operations need to be evaluated once again to see which category they come under, and the applicable regulatory standards must be complied with.

GENERATOR

The definition of "generator" found at 260.10 is "any person, by site, whose act or process produces hazardous waste identified or listed in Part 261 of this Chapter." Of course, all manufacturing facilities with process wastes, pollution control residuals or discarded commercial chemicals meeting this definition are generators.

However, most manufacturing facilities would also fit into another regulatory category. There is such a thing, however, as a generator (only). This is due to the discretion allowed generators, in some circumstances, regarding when a material becomes a waste, and when wastes have to be managed as hazardous.

Materials meeting the listing descriptions of the 261.31 and 261.32 lists (process residues, emission control dusts or wastewater treatment sludges) technically are hazardous wastes the moment they meet the listing description. As a practical matter, however, such wastes are not regulated, except for notification requirements, until they are removed from the process unit or pollution control device; otherwise, the unit or device would also be a storage facility subject to permit requirements. The point at which commercial chemical products become hazardous wastes is when they are intended to be discarded. However, the point at which used materials (e.g., spent solvents) become a waste is less clear. The guidance given in the preamble to Part 261 [45 FR 33095] says that this "generally occurs when intended use has ceased, and (the material) begins to be accumulated or stored for disposal, reuse or reclamation." Remember, a material must first be a waste before it can be hazardous, either by meeting a listing description or by possessing any of the characteristics.

Some examples may be instructive. Sludges in production process units (tanks, pipelines or pits) are not wastes until the process is stopped, the process solution is drained and the sludge is removed for proper waste management. A process solution, such as a solvent used in a degreaser, is not a waste until it no longer meets the user's requirements and is drained to replenish the degreaser tank. Another example would be the sediment ("bottoms") that often result from storage in tanks of raw material or product. According to 40 CFR 261.4(c), such materials are not subject to regulation (including notification) until the waste is removed from the unit, unless the unit is a surface impoundment or the waste remains in the unit longer than 90 days after the unit ceases to be operated for material or product storage.

The significance of these examples for the generator (only) category is that, generally, process and pollution control residuals do not become regulated as hazardous wastes until they are removed from the device in which they were generated. This is assuming that process units or pollution control devices have not been removed from service to serve as waste storage devices. If these process or pollution control residuals are removed offsite immediately after the unit or device is removed from service (e.g., in a vacuum truck used by an industrial cleaning contractor), no accumulation has occurred. Thus, the requirements for generators who accumulate or for generators who store under interim status would not apply.

It must be noted that the generator (only) category would apply just to manufacturing facilities where all hazardous wastes could be managed as described above. If other wastes are accumulated or stored after removal from the unit in which they were generated, or are accumulated or stored after the decision to discard, then the facility would fit better in one of the other regulatory categories.

One other point deserves mention—neither the act of hazardous waste generation or the owner or operator of a manufacturing facility where hazardous wastes are generated need a permit for hazardous waste generation nor the owner or operator of a manufacturing facility ating the wastes. The only hazardous waste management (HWM) activities requiring a permit are TSD. There are limited exceptions from the permit system for certain storage and treatment activities. Again, there is no such thing as a permit to generate a hazardous waste. A generator need only notify, obtain an EPA identification number, and follow the Part 262 standards. It is only when a generator also treats, stores or disposes of hazardous waste onsite that the permit system comes into play.

SMALL-QUANTITY GENERATOR

Certain hazardous waste generators are small-quantity generators, and as such, qualify for a set of special (reduced) requirements for the management of their hazardous wastes. The so-called "small quantity generator exclusion" is found at 40 CFR 261.5.

For all hazardous wastes except those covered by the acutely hazardous list [261.33(e)], a generator is a small-quantity generator as long as no more than 1000 kg (2200 lb or roughly three to four 55-gal drums) of hazardous waste is generated in any one calendar month. In addition, no more than 1000 kg of hazardous waste can be accumulated onsite at any one time if the generator is to remain a small-quantity generator.

In effect, the small-quantity generator is given an exemption from Parts 262–265 and 122–124 of the regulations in exchange for keeping his small quantities of hazardous wastes moving offsite to one of the several types of facilities given as management options in the regulations. The small-quantity exclusion level applies to the total amount of all hazardous waste streams at the facility, not to individual waste streams. Wastes that are hazardous only by virtue of possessing a characteristic (ignitability, reactivity, corrosivity or EP toxicity) and that are managed by recycling are not to be included in quantity determinations of small-generator status [261.5(c)].

Small-quantity generators should have sufficient documentation, such as estimated generation rates for every waste stream, and historical data, such as hauling records, to substantiate their claim. This documentation should include the determinations of the nonhazardous nature of other waste streams, and evidence of the disposition of wastes via recycling, if this option is used.

This information should be readily available, should there be any question on the part of state hazardous waste inspectors, landfill operators, insurance companies or corporate management.

With regard to wastes associated with the acutely hazardous list [261.33(e)], a different set of exclusion levels hold for generation in a calendar month or accumulation over a period of time. For such wastes, if more than 1 kg (2.2 lb) of commercial chemical products are discarded, or if more than 100 kg of any residue or contaminated soil, water or debris from the cleanup of a spill of such materials is generated, then all quantities of any acutely hazardous wastes are subject to full regulation, including notification.

It must be noted that interpretation of the regulation regarding small quantities of hazardous waste holds that if the exclusion level is exceeded for either hazardous waste or acutely hazardous wastes, then any quantities of both types of wastes that are onsite are fully subject to the complete set of regulations.

Another interesting interpretation of the small-quantity generator provisions is that a generator can move in and out of the small quantity "system," provided any accumulation of regulated quantities is for less than 90 days and that the 262.34 requirements are complied with during the periods of large-quantity generation. The time period for such accumulation onsite begins the day the accumulated wastes exceed the applicable exclusion level [261.5(f)]. A small-quantity generator that exceeded the exclusion level and that filed a permit application would have to undergo closure of the hazardous waste storage facility before reassuming small-quantity generator status.

It is important to note that some states have lower small-quantity exclusion levels or more stringent requirements than the federal regulations. Such requirements can include prior written approval for small quantities of hazardous waste proposed for land disposal. Chapter 8 discusses the regulatory requirements for small-quantity generators.

GENERATORS WHO RECYCLE HAZARDOUS WASTE

Many manufacturing facilities manage a portion of their hazardous wastes by the treatment process generically known as recycling, or use (or reuse) the wastes without any preparation in another process. Hazardous wastes managed by the activities known as use, reuse, recycling or reclamation are subject to a special (reduced) set of requirements. These activities can be performed on (1) onsite by the manufacturing facility; (2) by another manufacturing facility (after waste transfer); or (3) by a commercial offsite HWM facility.

The regulations distinguish between characteristic hazardous wastes (except sludges) that are recycled, and listed wastes, mixtures containing listed wastes and sludges. Basically, characteristic hazardous wastes that are recycled or reused are not subject to the regulations, including the notification requirement. Listed wastes and sludges that are transported, accumulated or stored before recycling or reuse are subject to full regulation with respect to such transportation or storage, including notification. If the latter provision does not seem much of an exemption, it is because it is not. The section of the regulations dealing with hazardous wastes that are used, reused, recycled and reclaimed is 261.6, and will be discussed in Chapter 9.

The important consideration in the determination of the applicability of this regulatory category is the actual disposition of the wastes generated by a manufacturing firm. The regulations provide the reduced requirements only for wastes that are beneficially used or reused, or legitimately recycled or reclaimed.

Although no definition or performance standard or time frame is given for the terms "beneficial" and "legitimate," common sense and historical uses and reclamation practices should serve as a guide. Generators should be suspicious of seemingly bogus or economically marginal schemes to recycle, such as the recovery of trace amounts (ppm levels) of metals from sludges, the use of wastes to reclaim "unproductive" land, or the recovery of heat values from materials with little or no Btu content.

If the company offering to recycle wastes in an economically marginal scheme goes bankrupt, the generator is faced with the distinct possibility of having to take his wastes back for proper disposal elsewhere.

If there is some doubt as to the propriety of a specific use or reuse, or of a particular recycling or recovery operation, contact your state solid waste official for an opinion. It is possible that the state in which a manufacturing facility is located may have more stringent requirements for the recycling of hazardous wastes. The state of Indiana, for example, requires all recycling operations to have a state permit, unless the hazardous wastes generated from the manufacturing process are recycled, recovered or reused at the same site by the generator [IC 13-7-8.5-5(e) and 320 IAC 4-3-7(a)(2)].

GENERATORS WHO ACCUMULATE HAZARDOUS WASTES

"Generators who accumulate" is a regulatory term for the persons qualifying for a special (reduced) set of requirements. Generators who accumulate perform the act of storage of a hazardous waste, and as such are technically owners or operators of a TSD facility, subject to the Part 265 standards and the permit requirements.

The regulatory definition of "storage" is found at 260.10 and is said to mean "the holding of hazardous waste for a temporary period, at the end of which the hazardous waste is treated, disposed of, or stored elsewhere." The regulations, however, allow owners or operators of storage facilities to comply only with the standards found at 262.34 under the following circumstances:

1. The owner or operator of the storage facility is also the person generating the wastes.
2. The waste is stored in the accumulation area for less than 90 days.

The 90-day accumulation period is only allowed for generators who place the waste in containers (typically 55-gal drums) or tanks. The 90-day accumulation period is thus not available to generators storing in surface impoundments (pits, ponds or lagoons) or waste piles.

As may be guessed, the most important aspects of the 262.34 standards are when the 90-day clock begins, and how a generator/accumulator is to document this period. The accumulation period begins when the first drop of hazardous waste is placed in the container or tank. It is at this time that the date of accumulation should be clearly marked on the container or tank. The container may continue to be filled next to some production process for several days; however, the time when the accumulation period begins is clear, and it is *not* when the filled drum is moved to storage.

A 1982 amendment to the 262.34 standards [47 FR 1248], delineates more clearly the EPA's intention regarding "accumulation areas," as the areas where wastes are stored for less than 90 days are called. One of the more significant points brought up in the preamble to that amendment is that a generator with a TSD area under interim status (pending disposition of the permit application) is allowed to have one or more accumulation areas. These areas can be loading docks where drums are staged before being moved to the storage area, or these areas can be where the wastes are actually generated and first placed in containers. Such areas can be enlarged and relocated without the restrictions on modifications to facilities during interim status [40 CFR 122.123(c)]. Of course, all such accumulation areas are subject to the requirements outlined in 262.34 (discussed in Chapter 10). In addition, accumulation areas are permissible for use with onsite recycling operations. Finally, the amendment made provisions for an emergency extension of the 90-day deadline, provided that the extension was necessary due to unforeseen, temporary or uncontrollable circumstances. This extension is at the discretion of the regional administrator of the EPA. Additionally, generators who accumulate are eligible for interim status, if a decision is made to pursue a storage permit [46 FR 60446]. It must be noted that there will be some delay before the various states adopt this amendment, thus making it applicable within their boundaries. However, many states have provisions for variances in their environmental statutes. Such provisions could be used in the interim, should the need arise.

It must be emphasized that the accumulation option is not as easy as it may seem from a first reading of 262.34. This is because 262.34 references requirements found elsewhere in the regulations, primarily in 40 CFR 262 and 265. There are definite requirements for generators who choose to use this option, and it is implicit that generators who fail to comply with these requirements are not (or will not be) allowed to take advantage of the accumulation area option. The requirements for generators who accumulate are discussed in Chapter 10.

GENERATORS WHO STORE HAZARDOUS WASTE UNDER INTERIM STATUS

Manufacturing facilities unable to take advantage of the 262.34 accumulation provisions for all of their hazardous waste storage activities are subject to the full brunt of the hazardous waste regulations. In other words, as owners or operators of hazardous waste storage facilities, such manufacturing firms must comply with all applicable provisions of 40 CFR 265, "Interim Status Standards for Owners and Operators of Hazardous Waste Treatment, Storage, and Disposal Facilities," and at the same time pursue a full RCRA permit under the provisions of 40 CFR 122 and 124.

As briefly discussed in Chapter 1, manufacturing firms that own or operate a hazardous waste storage facility had to meet certain requirements to qualify for interim status. Remember that interim status is a legal construct whereby a TSD facility is treated as if it had a permit until a final administrative disposition is made on its permit application. The three requirements necessary for a manufacturing firm to qualify for interim status are:

1. The hazardous waste TSD areas must have been in existence on or before November 19, 1980.
2. The owner or operator must have complied with the notification requirements of Section 3010 of RCRA on or before August 18, 1980.
3. The owner or operator must have filed Part A of the federal consolidated permit application (EPA forms 3510-1 and 3510-3) on or before November 19, 1980.

The possession of interim status is very important, for it prevents the manufacturing facility from having to cease HWM (storage) activities at the facility. A manufacturing firm that failed to obtain interim status and was not yet in possession of a full RCRA permit would have only the options of (1) sending hazardous wastes to an offsite facility with interim status, or (2) accumulating the hazardous wastes onsite for less than 90 days before sending the wastes offsite to a facility under interim status. In effect, a facility under interim status agrees to comply with the interim status standards (Part 265) in exchange for being allowed to continue hazardous waste management activities pending disposition of their permit application.

It is important to note that a storage facility under interim status is not to store hazardous wastes not specified in the Part A application, employ processes not specified in the application or exceed the design capacities specified in the application [122.23(b)]. There are, however, provisions for revising the Part A application to accommodate changes during interim status, under certain circumstances [122.23(c)].

If interim status is not obtained, or is revoked or denied, a manufacturing firm must follow the options given above while preparing a complete RCRA permit application (both Part A mentioned above and Part B, as required by 122.22 and 122.25). Offsite TSD must continue until a RCRA permit is obtained by meeting the applicable permit standards [40 CFR 264]. Facilities granted a full RCRA permit must comply with the Part 264 standards.

Remember that as states implement their own permit programs under the state hazardous waste management statutes, an analogous situation is created. A manufacturing facility must file a permit application with the state agency before the state deadline to be able to continue HWM (storage) activities. A manufacturing firm failing to do so would face having to have its hazardous wastes treated, stored or disposed offsite, regardless of whether the storage facility had interim status from EPA. This dual permit system will exist in some states until the state receives from EPA authorization to run the permit program. Once again, it is important that the reader check with the state hazardous waste management agency regarding the existence of any permit requirements. See Appendix 2 for a list of such agencies nationwide.

Manufacturing facilities that have not yet filed a permit application may still be granted interim status, or treated as if they have interim status. A *Federal Register* interpretation dated December 10, 1981, indicated that generators who have been accumulating may opt for an interim status storage facility should a decision be made or circumstances require storage of hazardous waste longer than 90 days [46 FR 60446].

Additionally, a *Federal Register* amendment [45 FR 76630] clarified the circumstances of interim status, indicating that an "interim status compliance letter" could, under some circumstances, be granted to facilities unable to meet the three requirements for interim status. An interim status compliance letter would, in effect, state that the facility would be treated by the EPA as if it had interim status for any enforcement purposes.

These options may prove valuable to manufacturing firms that, for some reason or another, failed to determine accurately their regulatory status or that desire to change that status.

One final note: in a *Federal Register* preamble [47 FR 1249], the EPA recognized that some generators filed what are termed "protective" or "precautionary" Part A permit applications. In other words, generators applied for a permit even though they were not required to do so by the regulations. For the most part, such protective filings were made by generators who wanted to have interim status for a storage area in case they had to hold wastes longer than 90 days. Also, some small-quantity generators filed in the event they became large-quantity generators for some reason. In this *Federal Register,* generators were encouraged to withdraw protective Part A filings by contacting their EPA regional offices. This is very good advice, especially for the generators who filed Part A permit applications without setting up a compliance program with respect to the Part 265 interim status standards for TSD facilities.

The regulatory requirements for hazardous waste storage areas of manufacturing firms are discussed in Chapter 11.

GENERATORS WHO SHIP HAZARDOUS WASTE OFFSITE

Although most manufacturing facilities in any of the categories discussed previously will also fall in this category, it is useful to discuss the transportation of hazardous wastes separately. Shipping hazardous wastes offsite places a generator under the regulatory jurisdiction of both the EPA and the U.S. Department of Transportation (DOT). Transportation of hazardous wastes comes under the purview of the DOT because hazardous wastes are considered a subset of DOT-regulated commodities known as "hazardous materials." DOT regulates the transportation of hazardous materials under the authority of the federal Hazardous Materials Transportation Act (HMTA). The Hazardous Material Transportation Regulations (HMTR) issued to implement the HMTA are found at 49 CFR 100–199.

By making a distinction between "onsite" and "offsite" transportation, the regulations regarding the transportation of hazardous wastes are not made to apply to movement of hazardous wastes within the generator's property. This allows for onsite HWM activities to take place without the necessity of a manifest or the other DOT pretransportation requirements.

The definition of "onsite" found in the regulations at 260.10 is unneccessarily complex and lengthy, but basically refers to property owned by the generator that is the same as or geographically contiguous to the property on which the waste was generated. This property may be divided by public or private right(s)-of-way (highways or railroads), and no manifest is necessary for moving the wastes across (as opposed to along) such right(s)-of-way to get the wastes to other portions of the generator's property.

The preamble to the regulations clarifies the definition of onsite (and thus the exemption from DOT transportation requirements) when wastes are moved across public or private right(s)-of-way. The entrance and exit of geographically contiguous property—for the movement of hazardous waste onsite without a manifest—must be directly across from each other [45 FR 33069].

The transportation of hazardous wastes offsite—from the site of generation to a TSD facility—must take place in compliance with both EPA and DOT standards. EPA and DOT standards make frequent reference to each other. This "joint-rulemaking" was used to minimize confusion and duplication. However, generators who offer hazardous waste for offsite transportation (known as "shippers" in DOT jargon) must have a working knowledge of both EPA and DOT regulations, and must use transporters ("carriers" in DOT jargon) who likewise need to know and abide by both EPA and DOT standards.

GENERATORS WHO TREAT HAZARDOUS WASTE BY AN EXEMPTED METHOD

The interim status standards found at 40 CFR 265 and the permit requirements of 40 CFR 122 do not apply to certain hazardous waste treatment operations, processes and methods. Of most interest to manufacturing facilities would be the exemptions granted to:

1. the owner or operator of a facility permitted, licensed or registered by a state to manage municipal or industrial solid waste, if the only hazardous wastes the facility treats, stores or disposes of are ex-

cluded from regulation by 261.5, "Special Requirements for Hazardous Waste Produced by Small Quantity Generators" [40 CFR 265.1(c)(5)];

2. the owner or operator of a facility that treats or stores a characteristic hazardous waste (except sludges) before beneficial use or re-use or legitimate recycling or reclamation under 40 CFR 261.6 [40 CFR 265.1(c)(6)] (for listed hazardous wastes, mixtures containing listed wastes and hazardous waste sludges that are transported or stored before recycling, the full brunt of the regulations applies to such transportation and storage, i.e., the treatment process or operation itself is not subject to the interim status standards or permit requirements; however, any ancillary storage prior to treatment is subject to the standards and permit requirements);

3. the owner or operator of a totally enclosed treatment facility, as defined in 260.10 [40 CFR 265.1(c)(9)];

4. the owner or operator of an elementary neutralization unit or a wastewater treatment unit as defined in 260.10 [40 CFR 265.1(c)(10)];

5. the owner or operator of a publicly owned treatment works (POTW, also known as a sewage treatment plant) that treats, stores or disposes of hazardous wastes [40 CFR 265.1(c)(3)],

6. persons with respect to those activities that are carried out immediately to contain or treat a spill of hazardous waste or material that becomes a hazardous waste when spilled (however, in the event of such a spill, owners and operators of TSD facilities otherwise subject to the regulations must comply with the preparedness and prevention, and contingency plan and emergency procedures requirements found in 40 CFR 265 [40 CFR 265.1(c)(11)]); and

7. the addition of absorbent material to waste in a container or the addition of waste to the absorbent material in a container, provided that these actions occur at the time waste is first placed in the containers [40 CFR 265.1(c)(13)].

It is important to note that the owner or operator of an exempted treatment facility can still be a generator of hazardous wastes, due to any spills, leaks, residues or sludges resulting from facility operations. Shipments of hazardous waste from such a facility must comply with the standards for generators found in 40 CFR 262. The 90-day accumulation provisions for generators [262.34] may be used by such facilities for the hazardous wastes generated at that facility. Chapter 13 explains the meaning and implications of exclusions 1–7 listed above.

This concludes Section 1. Armed with an understanding of the regulatory definitions of solid and hazardous wastes, the reader should now have made the following determinations:

1. What are all the wastes at the facility?
2. Which of the wastes are hazardous, using the regulatory definitions?
3. What HWM activities are occurring at the manufacturing facility, and which regulatory categories best fit such activities?

The next section explains the regulatory standards that apply to each of the categories. Sections 3 and 4 will then provide guidance in setting up a corporate compliance program.

SECTION 2

REGULATORY STANDARDS AND RESPONSIBILITIES

This section explains the regulatory standards for the categories of hazardous waste management activities most common at manufacturing firms. In many cases, a manufacturer will fall into more than one category. Knowledge of these standards is the necessary base on which to build a complete, least-cost compliance program, using the guidance given in Section 3.

Chapter 6

NONHAZARDOUS INDUSTRIAL
SOLID WASTES

Although this book is primarily focused on the proper management of wastes defined as "hazardous," some discussion of standards and good practices for the management of nonhazardous waste is necessary. This chapter is included because most manufacturing firms generate both hazardous and nonhazardous wastes, as well as wastes not meeting the definition of solid waste.

Federal and state statutes and regulations govern the disposition of nonhazardous solid wastes. However, such wastes are controlled primarily at the state level. Many states have special provisions for nonhazardous solid wastes from industrial sources, often termed "special wastes."

At the federal level, the Resource Conservation and Recovery Act (RCRA) prohibits "open dumping" of solid waste at Section 4005(c). The term "open dump" is defined in Section 1004(14) as "any facility or site where solid waste is disposed of which is not a sanitary landfill which meets the criteria promulgated under Section 4004 and which is not a facility for the disposal of hazardous waste." The federal guidelines promulgated under RCRA Section 4004 are the "Criteria for Classification of Solid Waste Disposal Facilities and Practices" [40 CFR 257]. These federal criteria are important because they have been used as guidelines by the various states in amending statutes prohibiting open dumps and revising state sanitary landfill regulations.

As mentioned earlier, nonhazardous industrial wastes are subject to regulation primarily at the state level, and should be managed properly. Proper management, for the most part, means disposing of such wastes at a sanitary landfill holding a valid state permit. At a minimum, such landfills must be well operated and should meet all of the requirements of the state's sanitary landfill regulations. It would be well advised not to send any such wastes to landfills under litigation or to

53

landfills being "phased out" due to poor geology or evidence of ground-water contamination. Such information can be obtained from your state solid waste management agency (Appendix 2). Ask to talk to the field inspector for the site in question.

It must be noted that some state regulatory agencies require some form of prior written approval to be obtained from them for hazardous and nonhazardous industrial wastes proposed for land disposal within their boundaries. These approvals, often called "permits" or "approval letters," are typically either for a specific waste stream (type) for a set period of time or are for each shipment of wastes. The approval is usually good only at a specific landfill.

A written request is typically required for such wastes, accompanied by relevant information on the waste and the process generating it. A detailed chemical and physical analysis is usually necessary. Although the state agency evaluation of such requests can take time, these requirements should be viewed as a blessing in disguise.

Because the purpose of such evaluations is to prevent land disposal of incompatible wastes and wastes unsuitable for land disposal, the state agency prevents or delays adverse environmental impacts from the landfill site. This in turn limits the liability of the waste generator, because his wastes unsuitable for land disposal are not placed in a landfill, but are required to be managed by other technologies, typically some form of waste treatment.

Some liquid or water-based wastes can be treated by an onsite National Pollutant Discharge Elimination System (NPDES)–permitted wastewater treatment plant, or can be discharged into a municipal sewer system for treatment by the municipal sewage treatment plant. The latter option should, of course, be exercised only with municipal approval.

One final point on land disposal needs to be made. Many nonhazardous industrial waste streams generated in large volumes have been managed on the property of the generator without the benefit of any permits. Onsite waste management practices such as using wastes as fill material, accumulating wastes in piles or heaps, and onsite dumping have been used for wastes such as fly ash, bottom ash, foundry sand and various sludges. Liquid and semisolid wastes have been stored or dewatered in industrial surface impoundments (pits, ponds and lagoons), or have been spread on land. Such onsite activities should be reevaluated in light of prohibitions on open dumping. The use of nonpermitted offsite property for the disposal of such wastes should also be examined and reviewed.

It is important to note that all such activities may need a permit from the state solid waste management agency and/or the state water pollution control agency. These requirements are relatively recent in many states.

It is advisable to work with state officials to close such waste management operations, or to upgrade them to meet permit standards. The use of unpermitted property for waste disposal can cause serious problems and consequences, so the proper goal should be to close and apply final cover to past sites, to close or upgrade existing sites, and to use only permitted sites in the future.

Chapter 7
GENERATORS

The regulatory requirements for manufacturing facilities as generators of hazardous wastes are quite simple. However, matters become much more involved when such manufacturing facilities accumulate or store hazardous wastes onsite, or offer hazardous wastes for offsite transportation. The regulatory standards for generators, generators who accumulate and generators who offer wastes for transportation offsite are found at 40 CFR 262.

Manufacturing facilities, as generators, are to:

1. determine if any solid wastes generated are hazardous according to the regulatory definition [262.11];
2. notify the U.S. Environmental Protection Agency (EPA) of hazardous waste activity on form 8700-12, and obtain an EPA identification number before treating, storing, disposing of, transporting or offering for transportation any hazardous waste (generators are also not to offer their hazardous waste to transporters or treatment, storage or disposal (TSD) facilities not having a valid EPA identification number [262.12]); and
3. keep records of any test results, waste analyses or other determinations made in accordance with 262.11 for at least three years from the date the waste was last sent to onsite or offsite TSD [262.40(c)].

As discussed in Chapter 5, the category of generator (only) is a very narrow one. Few manufacturing facilities could arrange their waste management activities so as to fall completely within this category. Manufacturing facilities in the generator (only) category should be aware of the additional requirements that come into play when hazardous wastes are offered for transportation offsite. These requirements include:

1. preparation of a manifest to accompany the movement of any hazardous wastes offsite;
2. following the manifest system procedures (described in Chapter 1);
3. compliance with U.S. Department of Transportation (DOT) requirements for packaging wastes, marking and labeling each package, and placarding the transportation vehicle;
4. monitoring the manifest tracking system to ensure that the wastes arrive at the designated facility (an exception report must be filed if a copy of the manifest is not returned to the generator by the designated TSD facility within 45 days);
5. submission of annual reports covering the types and amounts of hazardous wastes shipped offsite during the previous calendar year; and
6. keeping records of manifests, annual reports, exception reports, and any test results, waste analyses and determinations performed on facility waste streams.

Regulatory standards for generators who ship hazardous wastes offsite are discussed in Chapter 12. Regulatory standards for generators who accumulate are discussed in Chapter 10 and standards applicable to generators who store onsite are covered in Chapter 11.

Chapter 8

SMALL-QUANTITY GENERATORS

As mentioned in Chapter 5, a small-quantity generator qualifies for a set of special (reduced) requirements, provided his small quantities of hazardous waste are managed properly and not allowed to accumulate onsite above certain levels.

The special requirements for hazardous waste generated by small quantity generators are found at 40 CFR 261.5. A generator who, in a calendar month, generates less than 1000 kg (2200 lb or roughly three to four 55-gal drums) of hazardous wastes and who never accumulates more than 1000 kg onsite is a small-quantity generator. Different exclusion levels apply to generators of materials with a 261.33(e) listing (i.e., acutely hazardous wastes). These levels were explained in Chapter 5.

The hazardous wastes of a small-quantity generator are not subject to full regulation, including the notification requirement, as long as the small-quantity generator complies with a set of reduced requirements. These reduced requirements are found at 261.5(g). The small-quantity generator must:

1. determine the hazardous/nonhazardous nature of all solid wastes generated (discussed in Chapter 4); and
2. not accumulate quantities of hazardous or acutely hazardous waste greater than their respective exclusion levels. (if these levels are exceeded, notification must be given and the applicable standards of 40 CFR 262–265 and 122 must be met, beginning the day the wastes exceed the applicable exclusion level.)

The hazardous waste of a small-quantity generator must be (1) treated or disposed of onsite at a permitted facility; (2) transported offsite to a permitted facility; or (3) managed on- or offsite at a facility that uses, reuses, recycles or reclaims the waste, or treats the waste before such use.

As used here, "permitted facilities" include those with a full Resource Conservation and Recovery Act (RCRA) permit, treatment, storage or disposal (TSD) facilities under interim status, and facilities "permitted, licensed, or registered" by a state to manage municipal or industrial solid waste (i.e., sanitary landfills).

Paragraph 261.5(h) holds that a mixture of nonhazardous wastes and hazardous wastes subject to the reduced requirements is subject only to the reduced requirements, unless the mixture meets any of the characteristics of a hazardous waste. Remember that one of the requirements for a small-quantity generator is that he determine if any of his solid wastes (including mixtures of hazardous and nonhazardous waste) are hazardous.

The reduced requirements for mixtures (that do not meet the characteristics) apply even if the mixture exceeds the applicable quantity limitations. However, paragraph 261.5(i) holds that if a hazardous waste exceeding the exclusion level is mixed with a solid waste, then the entire mixture is subject to full regulation.

The reduced requirements for small-quantity generators found at 261.5 do indeed give manufacturing firms greater leeway in managing their small quantities of hazardous waste. Of course, such small quantities should be managed by reuse or recycling, if possible. Remember that small-generator status does not allow the manufacturing firm to improperly manage its hazardous wastes.

Many commercial hazardous waste management facilities are offering, in conjunction with transportation firms, what are known as "milk-run" services to small-quantity generators or firms with small amounts of recyclable wastes. Milk runs are basically regular multistop routes where small quantities of waste are picked up from different generators. Such services promote recycling and make it easier for firms to stay under the 1000-kg accumulation limit or within the 90-day accumulation period. The availability of such services should be explored with commercial hazardous waste management firms.

At the present time, many of the wastes of small-quantity generators are managed by sanitary landfill and thus are disposed of in conjunction with municipal solid wastes (i.e., trash, garbage and refuse). The hazardous waste regulations do not require a small-quantity generator to tell the landfill operator that hazardous wastes are being shipped to the landfill, nor do they require that the generator alert the landfill operator of the hazards posed by the waste, or of any precautions to be taken during disposal. Regardless of the absence of legal language to that effect, good business practices, common sense and self-interest all point to the propriety of such a notification to the landfill operator. Even small quantities of hazardous wastes can cause serious problems at the landfill when the wastes are compacted by a hot bulldozer and mixed with other wastes. The potentials for fire or explosion are obvious.

In some states, the federal standards for small-quantity generators have been preempted by more stringent state requirements. Exclusion levels in the state regulations are smaller and/or additional requirements are imposed. Prior written approval may be necessary to take even small quantities of hazardous waste to a municipal landfill. Again, it is necessary to check with your state solid waste official.

Chapter 9

GENERATORS WHO RECYCLE HAZARDOUS WASTES

As discussed in Chapter 5, hazardous wastes that are beneficially used or reused, or legitimately recycled or reclaimed, or accumulated, stored or treated before such activities are subject to special (reduced) requirements. Many manufacturing firms could possibly manage a portion of their hazardous waste by use, reuse, recycling or reclamation, hereafter referred to as "recycling." That portion of their wastes so managed would be subject only to the reduced requirements. The remainder of their hazardous wastes would be subject to full regulation. The act of recycling can take place at the manufacturing facility generating the waste, at another manufacturing facility or at a commercial hazardous waste management (HWM) facility. Chapters 14 and 15 give examples of waste management options that constitute use, reuse, recycling, or reclamation.

The special requirements for hazardous waste that is used, reused, recycled or reclaimed are found at 40 CFR 261.6. These requirements make an important distinction between characteristic hazardous wastes (except sludges) that are recycled and listed wastes, mixtures containing listed wastes and sludges that are managed by recycling. Recycled wastes that are hazardous solely because of a characteristic (ignitability, corrosivity, reactivity or extraction procedure (EP) toxicity) and are not sludges (remember that sludges are pollution control residues) are not subject to regulation under the federal HWM system.

Listed hazardous wastes, hazardous waste sludges and mixtures containing listed wastes that are transported or stored before being used, reused, recycled or reclaimed are subject to regulation only with regard to their transportation or storage. As the regulation [261.6(b)] states, such wastes are

> subject to the following requirements with respect to transportation or storage:

(1) Notification requirements under Section 3010 of RCRA
(2) Part 262 of this Chapter
(3) Part 263 of this Chapter
(4) Subparts A, B, C, D and E of Part 264 of this Chapter
(5) Subparts A, B, C, D, E, G, H, I, J and L of Part 265 of this Chapter
(6) Parts 122 and 124 of this Chapter with respect to storage facilities.

In essence, a generator who transports or stores a listed hazardous waste (or sludge) before recycling must follow the same standards for storage as generators who accumulate (Chapter 10) or generators who store (Chapter 11). Transportation standards are the same as those for generators who ship offsite (Chapter 12).

The implication of the limitation of regulatory coverage to transportation and storage is that the waste recycling process itself or any manufacturing operations in which the waste is recycled does not require a treatment permit. Additionally, such processes or operations are not subject to the standards for treatment, storage or disposal (TSD) facilities.

The purpose of the above regulatory situation is to encourage recycling of hazardous waste by not subjecting any processes or operations to the full brunt of the facility standards [Part 265] and permit requirements [Part 122].

Remember, however, that the regulatory coverage of transportation and storage applies to the waste itself, not just to the generator. As a result, any commercial recycling facility or other manufacturing facility where the wastes are recycled must have permitted storage facilities or storage facilities under interim status. Further, they must follow the standards for such facilities and comply with any applicable transportation standards.

It must be noted that facilities, processes or operations that recycle hazardous waste *treat* such wastes, according to the regulatory definition of treatment [260.10]. Under the definition of hazardous waste [261.3(c)], any solid waste generated from the treatment, storage or disposal of a hazardous waste is a hazardous waste unless it meets the criteria of 261.3(d). These criteria are:

1. The solid waste does not exhibit any of the characteristics of a hazardous waste.
2. In the case of a listed waste, a waste containing a listed waste or a waste derived from a listed waste, it must also have been excluded from 261.3(c) under 262.20 and 260.22.

Therefore, residues from recycling any listed hazardous waste must also be managed as hazardous, unless they are delisted and not "captured" by the characteristics.

The impact of these provisions is that recycling operations are likely to result in the generation of a hazardous waste, by virtue of any residue, still bottom, sludge, etc. As such, these residues must be managed according to the regulatory standards, and the recycler becomes a generator (if he is not already).

It must be noted that the 261.31 list, "Hazardous Wastes from Nonspecific Sources," includes any still bottoms and sludges from the recovery of the various solvents specified within each listing. Each listing of solvents includes language to that effect.

There are several other regulatory provisions that affect generators who recycle. Treatment residues from onsite hazardous waste recycling operations conducted by small-quantity generators do not count toward generation rates [261.5(d)(2)]. Further, characteristic hazardous wastes (except sludges) managed by on- or offsite recycling are not to be included in quantity determinations for small-generator status.

Also of interest is the fact that generators who recycle onsite are allowed to have accumulation areas governed by 262.34 [47 FR 1251–262.10(b)]. This means that areas or tanks where wastes are held to accumulate sufficient quantities for batch recycling operations do not necessarily need a storage permit, as long as no wastes remain in storage longer than 90 days. Any storage of listed hazardous wastes (or sludges) for recycling onsite for longer than 90 days does require a permit and must meet the storage facility standards (Chapter 11).

Once again it is necessary to point out that the state in which a generator is located, or the state in which the recycling operation is located (if in different states) may have different or more stringent requirements. Contact the appropriate state solid waste management agency(ies) to obtain copies of any regulatory requirements for recycling that differ from the federal scheme.

Chapter 10

GENERATORS WHO ACCUMULATE HAZARDOUS WASTES ONSITE LESS THAN NINETY DAYS

The regulatory category of "generators who accumulate" describes at least a portion of the hazardous waste management (HWM) activities at a majority of hazardous waste–generating manufacturing firms. This category encompasses containerized storage at waste-generating areas, any temporary storage at staging areas (i.e., loading docks) before offsite transportation, as well as any accumulation before onsite or offsite waste management at storage, treatment or disposal (TSD) areas under interim status.

The regulatory provision allowing storage by generators for less than 90 days without a permit (262.34, "Accumulation Time") was established to prevent undue interference with the manufacturing process itself. Such interference was avoided by not requiring Resource Conservation and Recovery Act (RCRA) permits for areas where hazardous wastes are accumulated temporarily. The regulations found at 262.34 specify a set of standards applicable to such temporary accumulation. As mentioned in Chapter 5, the accumulation option is not as easy as merely moving the waste offsite or to an onsite TSD facility within 90 days. Section 262.34 makes extensive reference to regulatory standards found in 40 CFR 265. Although the regulatory standards for generators who accumulate are not as comprehensive as those for generators who store under interim status, the 262.34 standards still necessitate a compliance program.

It may be useful to list the requirements printed in Section 262.34(a) of the regulations. Section 262.34 was amended by the U.S. Environmental Protection Agency (EPA) on January 11, 1982 [47 FR 1251]. This amendment deleted the requirements that hazardous wastes be packaged, marked and labeled according to U.S. Department of Transportation (DOT) requirements during the accumulation period. A generator is allowed to accumulate hazardous waste onsite for 90 days or less without a permit or without having interim status (by applying for a permit) provided that:

> (1) The waste is placed in containers and the generator complies with Subpart I of 40 CFR Part 265, or the waste is placed in tanks and the generator complies with Subpart J of 40 CFR Part 265 except § 265.193;
> (2) The date upon which each period of accumulation begins is clearly marked and visible for inspection on each container;
> (3) While being accumulated on-site, each container and tank is labeled or marked clearly with the words, "Hazardous Waste"; and
> (4) The generator complies with the requirements for owners or operators in Subparts C and D in 40 CFR Part 265 and with § 265.16.

Generators who accumulate hazardous wastes longer than 90 days are considered operators of a storage facility, fully subject to the requirements of 40 CFR 264 and 265, as well as the permit requirements of 40 CFR 122. However, Section 262.34(b) provides that the generator may petition to be granted an extension to the 90-day period. Such an extension may be granted by the EPA and/or the state regulatory agency if the wastes must remain onsite for longer than 90 days due to unforeseen, temporary and uncontrollable circumstances. An extension of up to 30 days may be granted on a case-by-case basis.

The following are the regulatory references found in 262.34 along with an explanation of the requirements found at each section. Although the explanation closely follows the regulatory language, the reader is advised to go to the regulations themselves should there be any question as to meaning or relationships to other regulatory requirements. While reading the remainder of the chapter, it should be kept in mind that the Part 265 regulations extensively referenced in 262.34 are oriented primarily toward commercial (offsite) HWM facilities. When the term "facility" is used in the regulations, it is used to refer to HWM facilities. While this would include all or nearly all of the buildings, equipment and operations of a commercial hazardous waste management facility, the term "facility" has much more limited application with respect to the operations of a manufacturing firm. The regulatory term "facility" would have meaning for the purposes of regulatory compliance only for areas where hazardous wastes are treated, stored or disposed of onsite. For generators who accumulate, the term "facility" would apply only to areas where hazardous wastes are accumulated. The regulatory definition of "facility," found at 40 CFR 260.10, is as follows:

> all contiguous land, and structures, other appurtenances, and improvements on the land, used for treating, storing, or disposing of hazardous waste. A facility may consist of several treatment, storage, or disposal operational units (e.g., one or more landfills, surface impoundments, or combinations of them).

USE AND MANAGEMENT OF CONTAINERS
[40 CFR 265, Subpart I]

Condition of Containers [40 CFR 265.171]

Containers used for holding hazardous waste must be in good condition. If the container becomes damaged, deteriorated or begins to leak, the wastes should be transferred to a container that is in good condition.

Typically, wastes are accumulated in the containers that are going to be used to ship the wastes offsite. This minimizes the time, labor and spills/leaks that accompany the transfer of wastes from one container to another.

The Part 262 requirements for generators specify that hazardous waste must be packaged (containerized) according to DOT specifications before offsite transportation. Usually, this requirement is met by placing the wastes in 55-gal drums that meet DOT specifications for the type of material to be transported. For the most part, this means that the standard 17H open-head drum (Figure 4a) is used for solids and sludges, and the standard 17E closed-head (bung-opening) drum (Figure 4b) is used for liquids. Certain waste materials, such as acids and caustics, require drums with liners and/or drums made of corrosion-resistant steel. If there is a question as to the proper type of container, refer to the hazardous materials table [49 CFR 172.101] for reference to the packaging requirements for specific hazardous materials. Other sources of information include barrel vendors, transporter contacts or regulatory agencies such as the DOT and the state hazardous waste management agency.

Compatibility of Waste with Container [40 CFR 265.172]

Containers used for holding hazardous wastes must not be deteriorated by the waste. This will require the use of containers with liners,

Figure 4.   Standard drums: A = 17H (open-head); B = 17E (closed head, bung-opening).

stainless steel containers or plastic drums for certain wastes, such as strong acids or caustics.

Management of Containers [40 CFR 265.173]

Containers holding hazardous wastes must always be closed during storage. This means that the bungs in a closed-head drum must be present and tight. For open-head drums, the head (and head cover gasket) must be present and the ring holding the cover must be secured tightly. The only time containers can be opened during storage is to add or remove waste.

Containers holding hazardous waste are to be managed to avoid rupturing or otherwise damaging the container, or causing the container to leak. This may require physically locating the containers away from areas with heavy equipment traffic. Many drums have been punctured or damaged by forklift traffic. Methods used to move containers should not damage or deform the container. Another consideration is the opening of containers. The author has seen drums that were punctured to provide additional vents to allow for faster transfer of wastes from container to container. Samples are occasionally taken by driving a spike through a drum lid to provide access to sampling equipment. Needless to say, such actions prevent the container from ever again being closed.

Additionally, solvents or other materials with high vapor pressure should not be stored in black drums in direct sunlight. Many leaks have been caused by expansion of the contents of a waste container. Occasionally, vapor pressure will permanently deform the drum, making it unsuitable for shipping. Also, some waste materials must be protected from freezing. There are several means of avoiding leaks from expansion of contents, including:

1. allowing expansion room when filling drums;
2. storing containers under a roof in ventilated areas;
3. using storage areas not in direct sunlight, when wastes must be stored outside; and
4. using light-colored drums when wastes are stored outside.

Inspections [40 CFR 265.174]

Weekly inspections must be made of container storage (accumulation) areas. Although not specifically mentioned, there should be some documentation of: (1) what is looked for during an inspection; (2) that the inspections are actually performed; and (3) any remedial action taken as a result of conditions discovered during the inspection.

An inspection checklist could be developed to ensure that whoever inspects the facility on a weekly basis knows what to look for. By developing a checklist, the inspections could be assigned to personnel not highly trained in waste management, i.e., security guards, industrial hygenists, foremen or laborers.

A sample inspection form is provided in Table III. Some items not required to be inspected by the regulations have been included for possible use. Inspection of these items would constitute good management practice. Merely performing inspections and noting deficiencies is not enough. Remedial actions must be taken to prevent small problems from becoming big problems. For example, the contents of corroded or damaged drums should be transferred to another container before the contents leak out of the original container. To promote this,

Table III.   Hazardous Waste Container Accumulation Area Inspection Form (Example)

Area[a] _____   Number of Containers _____

Date and Time _____   Number of Empty Containers _____

Inspector's Name _____

Reviewed by _____

Inspection Item	Potential Problems	Status (Acceptable or Unacceptable)	Remarks or Observations	Remedial Actions Necessary	Date Remedial Actions Performed
Adequate Aisle Space	Barrels placed too close to properly inspect or remove				
Container Stacking	Containers stacked more than two high; containers not on pallets				
Condition of Containers	Deteriorated, damaged, corroded, rusted or leaking drums; drums damaged or leaking from expansion of contents				
Sealing of Containers	Containers not stored closed; containers without bungs or lids; bungs or lids not tight on container				
Labels	Labels identifying generator, contents and accumulation date are missing or faded				
Accumulation Start Date	Not present or not readable; 90-day period has passed				
Segregation of Materials	Wastes not segregated by type; wastes not in proper aisle				
Emergency Equipment	Fire extinguishers, spill absorbent or other necessary equipment is not available at the accumulation area				

Inspection Item	Potential Problems	Status (Acceptable or Unacceptable)	Remarks or Observations	Remedial Actions Necessary	Date Remedial Actions Performed
Drainage	Rainwater or other liquids are ponding around drums				
Evidence of Leakage	Deteriorated containers are leaking; pumping of wastes or filling of containers has resulted in spilled material not cleaned up				
Fence and Storage Pad	General damage; cracks, uneven settlement or erosion of storage pad				
Unacceptable Material	Presence of containers of garbage or refuse in storage area; presence of nonwaste containers; presence of equipment or materials that are not supposed to be in the area				
Surrounding Area	Presence of activities or equipment posing a potential source of spark or flame (examples include welding, intense heat sources, smoking areas)				
"No Smoking" Signs	Absence of such signs; deterioration or damage to such signs				
Separation of Incompatible Wastes	Incompatible wastes in same general area; incompatible wastes not separated by a berm, dike or wall				

ᵃFor example, loading dock, store room, storage pad.

the sample inspection sheet has spaces for the type of remedial action necessary and for the remedial action performed and the date it was performed. The person inspecting must sign the form, and, ideally, the form should be reviewed by a person responsible for hazardous waste management before the form is filed. The inspection forms become part of the record-keeping system necessary to document compliance, and should be kept for at least three years from the date of inspection.

Special Requirements for Ignitable or Reactive Waste [40 CFR 265.176]

Areas where ignitable or reactive hazardous wastes are accumulated should be located at least 50 ft from the facility property line. Such wastes should also be separated and protected from sources of ignition or reaction, e.g., open flames, smoking, cutting, welding, hot surfaces, frictional heat, sparks and radiant heat. "No smoking" signs should be posted wherever there is a hazard from ignitable or reactive wastes.

It is possible that the plant layout or plant operations are such that ignitable or reactive wastes cannot be separated and protected from ignition sources without violating the rule requiring 50 ft of separation from the property line. If this is the case, it is recommended that the wastes remain near the property line and a request for a variance from the application of 40 CFR 265.176 be filed with EPA and the state regulatory agency.

Special Requirements for Incompatible Wastes [40 CFR 265.177]

The generator is to determine whether any two waste streams are incompatible. Guidance in this determination is provided by Appendix V of 40 CFR 265. Appendix V provides examples of potentially incompatible wastes, waste components and materials. These wastes, components and materials are organized into groups for purposes of outlining the potential adverse consequences of contact between incompatible groups. Appendix V is reprinted in Appendix 3 of this book for handy reference. Another source of information regarding potentially incompatible wastes is "A Method for Determining the Compatibility of Hazardous Wastes," EPA-600/2-80-076, U.S. EPA (1980).

Incompatible wastes, or incompatible wastes and materials must not be placed in the same container for storage purposes. Further, hazardous waste cannot be placed in an unwashed container that previously held an incompatible waste or material.

Finally, incompatible hazardous wastes and wastes incompatible with nearby materials must be separated or protected. The purpose of the separation or protection is to prevent adverse consequences that could result if incompatible wastes are mixed. This mixture could result, for example, if a container were accidently punctured or leaked due to deterioration of the container.

Separation of incompatible wastes is as simple as storing them in different locations. Sufficient distance should be allowed to avoid any possibility of mixture or contact should containers of one (or both) type(s) of waste be damaged or leak. It is important to remember that strong corrosives, when spilled or leaked, can rapidly deteriorate any nearby containers. This is another possible avenue of contact between incompatible wastes that can be avoided by separation.

Protection of incompatible wastes from contact with each other is the second alternative offered for meeting the regulatory requirements for storing incompatible wastes. Protection refers to physical structures or devices that will prevent the contact of incompatible wastes, even if containers of both types leak simultaneously. Protective devices allow for incompatible wastes to be stored in close proximity. Protective devices include berms, dikes or walls. If waste storage areas are bermed or diked to prevent mixing, any drainage ways and collection sumps must be designed as separate systems, to prevent mixing of any collected liquids from the separated areas, which may contain the incompatible wastes.

TANKS [40 CFR 265 Subpart J, except 265.193]

Storage of ignitable or reactive hazardous wastes in tanks must be conducted so that it does not:

1. generate extreme heat, pressure, fire, explosion or violent reaction;
2. produce uncontrolled toxic mists, fumes, dusts or gases in sufficient quantities to threaten human health;
3. produce uncontrolled flammable fumes or gases in sufficient quantities to pose a risk of fire or explosions;
4. damage the structural integrity of the device or facility containing the waste; or
5. through other like means threaten human health or the environment. [40 CFR 265.192(a), as it references 265.17(b)].

Hazardous wastes must not be placed in a tank if they could cause the tank or its inner liner to rupture, leak, corrode or otherwise fail before the end of its intended life [265.192(b)].

Uncovered tanks must be operated to ensure at least 2 ft (60 cm) of freeboard, unless the tank is equipped with a containment structure (e.g., dike or trench), a drainage control system or a diversion structure (e.g., standby tank) with a capacity that equals or exceeds the volume of the top 2 ft of the tank [265.192(c)].

Where hazardous waste is continuously fed into a tank, the tank must be equipped with a means to stop this inflow (e.g., a waste feed cutoff system or bypass system to a standby tank) [265.192(d)].

The owner or operator of a tank must inspect, where present:

1. discharge control equipment (e.g., waste feed cutoff systems, bypass systems and drainage systems), at least once each operating day, to ensure that it is in good working order [265.194 (a)(1)];
2. data gathered from monitoring equipment (e.g., pressure and temperature gauges), at least once each operating day, to ensure that the tank is being operated according to its design [265.194 (a)(2)];
3. the level of waste in the tank, at least once each operating day, to ensure compliance with 265.192(c) [265.194(a)(3)];
4. the construction materials of the tank, at least weekly, to detect corrosion or leaking of fixtures or seams [265.194(a)(4)]; and
5. the construction materials of and the area immediately surrounding discharge confinement structures (e.g., dikes), at least weekly, to detect erosion or obvious signs of leakage (e.g., wet spots or dead vegetation) [265.194(a)(5)].

At closure, all hazardous waste and hazardous waste residues must be removed from tanks, discharge control equipment and discharge confinement structures [40 CFR 265.197].

Ignitable or reactive waste must not be placed in a tank, unless the waste is stored in such a way that it is protected from any material or conditions that may cause the waste to ignite or react [40 CFR 265.198(a)(2)].

The owner or operator of a facility that stores ignitable or reactive waste in covered tanks must comply with National Fire Protection Association (NFPA) buffer zone requirements for tanks, contained in Tables 2-1 through 2-6 of the "Flammable and Combustible Code—1977" [40 CFR 265.198(b)].

Incompatible wastes, or incompatible wastes and materials must not be placed in the same tank, unless 265.17(b) is complied with [40 CFR 265.199]. Appendix V of 40 CFR 265 provides examples of potentially incompatible wastes. See above for requirements of 265.17(b), as referenced by 265.192(a).

ACCUMULATION START DATE [40 CFR 262.34(a)(2)]

The accumulation start date for each container is to be marked clearly on each container. Markings can be applied by indelible marker, spray paint and stencils, or a label with a space for marking the start date. Figure 5 (Chapter 19) provides an example of just such a label. The accumulation start date marking must be visible for inspection.

The requirement that the accumulation start date be clearly visible for inspection is to allow ready determination by regulatory personnel of the compliance of a generator who accumulates with the 90-day limitation. This may require that the accumulation start date be marked on opposite sides of the container. Alternatively, all containers could be oriented so as to have the start date marking easily visible. Either alternative will necessitate some form of orderly arrangement of containers. Otherwise, the inspection requirements (accumulation start date and container storage areas) cannot be met in good faith. These inspection requirements can be met easily by arranging containers in rows that are two containers wide, with at least two feet separating each row. Further, containers should be stacked no more than two high. Containers can be placed on pallets if forklifts are to be used to move containers. Placing containers close together and/or stacking containers higher than two high clearly prevents thorough inspections and does not constitute good practice. Container storage is discussed further in Chapter 19.

LABELING [40 CFR 262.34(a)(3)]

Each container or tank must be labeled or marked clearly with the words "hazardous waste." As with the accumulation start date, the words "hazardous waste" can be marked with indelible marker, spray-painted on the container or tank, or can be attached by a label. An example of a label that meets the requirements of marking the accumulation start date as well as of affixing the words "hazardous waste" is found in Figure 5 (Chapter 19).

To eliminate the necessity of rotating containers to make the accumulation start date visible, it may be desirable to place two such labels on each container.

PREPAREDNESS AND PREVENTION [40 CFR 265, Subpart C]

A preparedness and prevention program, required of generators who accumulate as well as of generators who store, is just what the name implies. The prevention aspect of such a program involves the proper operation and maintenance of accumulation areas to minimize the risk of fire, explosion, leaks, spills or damaged containers. The generator who accumulates or stores is not given much guidance or specific directives in establishing such a program. The regulations merely specify a performance standard—that the accumulation areas be maintained and operated so as to minimize the possibility of a fire, explosion or unplanned sudden (accidental) or gradual release of hazardous waste or hazardous waste constituents to the air, soil or surface water.

The major portion of the prevention aspect of a preparedness and prevention program would be the adherence to the standards set out Subpart J, "Tanks," of 40 CFR 265. Further discussion of best management practices as they apply to the storage of hazardous waste is found in Chapter 19.

Subpart C is much more specific with respect to the preparedness aspect of a preparedness and prevention program. There are equipment requirements, requirements to test and maintain equipment, requirements for access to alarm systems and external communications, required aisle space for movement of emergency equipment, and required arrangements with local authorities. What follows is a section-by-section explanation of Subpart C, "Preparedness and Prevention."

Maintenance and Operation of Facility [40 CFR 265.31]

Accumulation areas must be maintained and operated to minimize the possibility of a fire, explosion or any unplanned sudden or gradual release of hazardous waste or hazardous waste constituents to air, soil or surface water that could threaten human health or the environment.

Required Equipment [40 CFR 265.32]

Generators who accumulate must find out the type and degree of hazard(s) posed by the different facility waste streams. A full complement of specified emergency equipment is required to be available at each accumulation area unless none of the hazards posed by the wastes handled could require a particular kind of equipment specified. The specified equipment includes:

1. internal communications or alarm system;
2. telephone or two-way radio at the scene of operations capable of summoning external assistance;
3. portable fire extinguishers;
4. fire control equipment (including special equipment using foam, inert gas, or dry chemicals as the extinguishing agent);
5. spill control equipment;
6. decontamination equipment; and
7. water at adequate volume and pressure to supply water hoses, foam extinguishing equipment, or automatic sprinklers or spray systems.

Table IV gives, for some common waste streams, a suggested evaluation of the necessity of particular kinds of emergency equipment specified above. Each waste stream is different, and it is the generator's responsibility to gather all readily available data on the types and degree of hazard posed by each waste stream. Material safety data sheets for the components of the waste, as well as laboratory analyses and determinations are the starting points in the search for such information. Remember that if any waste requires a given kind of emergency equipment, that equipment *must* be available.

Given that the generator has made a determination as to which kinds of emergency equipment are required at the accumulation area(s), it might be instructive to give examples of each category.

Internal Communications or Alarm System [40 CFR 265.32(a)]

Presumably, this communication or alarm system would be used by workers handling hazardous wastes to summon internal assistance or to recommend evacuation, should there be a fire, explosion or major leak while wastes are being moved or transferred from container to container. It is important to note that such a device does not have to be at the actual accumulation area, provided the workers handling hazardous wastes have visual or voice contact with another employee who does have immediate access to such a device.

Just what constitutes an internal communications or alarm system is unclear. The regulations provide little guidance. It is possible that a variety of devices could meet the standard. Such devices include:

Table IV.   Common Waste Streams and Evaluation of Emergency Equipment Requirements

Waste Stream	Type of Hazard	Required Equipment[a]							Comments
		1	2	3	4	5	6	7	
Ignitable Liquids (solvents, DOT flammable or combustible materials)	Fire, explosion, spill, leak	√	√	√ and/ or	√	√	?	√a	a = if necessary for 4
Reactive Wastes, Solid or Liquid (cyanide- or sulfide-containing wastes)	Fire, explosion, spill, leak, release of toxic fumes	√	√	√ and/ or	√	√	?	√b	b = unless the wastes are water-reactive
Corrosive Liquids (acids, alkalis, cleaning solutions)	Release of toxic fumes, spill, leak, may cause rapid deterioration of other containers if spilled or leaked	√	√	?	?	√	√c	√d	c = neutralization agents; d = unless water will react with strong acids or bases
Toxic Liquids (certain nonflammable solvents, organic liquids, plating solutions)	Release of toxic fumes; spill or leak may disable industrial or municipal wastewater treatment operations	√	√			√	√		
Nonpumpable EP-Toxic Sludges (industrial wastewater treatment sludges)	Groundwater pollution					√e	?		e = shovels

[a]1 = internal communications or alarm system; 2 = telephone or two-way radio at the scene of operations capable of summoning external assistance; 3 = portable fire extinguishers; 4 = fire control equipment (including special equipment using foam, inert gas or dry chemicals as the extinguishing agent; 5 = spill control equipment; 6 = decontamination equipment; 7 = water at adequate volume and pressure to supply water hoses, foam extinguishing equipment, or automatic sprinklers or spray systems.

1. an internal alarm or communication device that would alert a guard station or managerial office of a problem (the guard or plant manager or emergency coordinator could then alert internal fire brigades, summon maintenance staff or could sound a general plant evacuation alarm, if necessary);

2. an internal telephone system that gives access to a plant intercom; and

3. a simple alarm, such as a compressed air horn, that would alert nearby workers to summon assistance.

Telephone or Hand-Held Two-Way Radio [40 CFR 265.32(b)]

It is obvious that this device is meant to summon assistance from external sources. Telephones and two-way radios are given as examples. Once again, employees handling hazardous wastes at accumulation areas are to have immediate access to such a device, unless they are in visual or voice contact with another employee who has such access. If access to alarms and telephones is to be provided through visual or voice contact with another employee (presumably some distance away from the accumulation area), it would be advisable to have a written waste handling standard operating procedure (SOP) to that effect. Such a SOP would require the use of an "extra" employee to man the phone or alarm system whenever wastes are handled (poured, mixed, or transferred in or out of containers) at the accumulation area(s). This written SOP would be necessary to document compliance by use of visual or voice contact rather than having such devices in the immediate vicinity of each accumulation area.

Portable Fire Extinguishers [40 CFR 265.32(c)]

Fire extinguishers should be available within arm's reach of waste-handling employees; otherwise, any fire started will very likely be out of hand once the employee leaves the scene of operations to obtain a fire extinguisher. Needless to say, the extinguishers available to the accumulation area must be of the proper type to fight the type of fire that could result from the particular wastes present.

Fire Control Equipment

If the type or amounts of ignitable, flammable or combustible wastes present require more response than is available from portable fire extinguishers, thought might be given to making fire control equipment available. Such equipment would include

1. sprinkler systems;
2. fire hose;
3. large, wheeled extinguishers;
4. foam-producing equipment; or
5. inert gas systems.

It would make sense to contact your fire insurance carrier and local fire department to obtain input on the types of fire control equipment desirable. It is likely that a reduction in premiums could result from better fire protection.

Spill Control Equipment

Spill control equipment can be as simple as bags of industrial absorbent (oil dry, expanded clay or Hazorb) or as complicated as spill booms or vacuum-type spill cleanup devices. Areas where wastes are pumped, poured, mixed or transferred from container to container should have spill absorbent readily available. Likewise, absorbent should be available when moving containers. Ready access to absorbent will minimize cleanup costs and problems.

Decontamination Equipment

The regulations provide no examples of what constitutes decontamination equipment. Obviously, spilled materials will cause areas of the storage base to need decontamination. Likewise, any protective equipment worn by workers responding to a spill will need to be decontaminated. Spill absorbent will need to be collected and containerized. Contaminated equipment and floors will need to be washed off, and the wash water treated properly. Spills of acids or bases may require neutralization. Contaminated soils may require removal. Any damaged drums may need to be placed in overpack containers. The need for decontamination equipment will have to be evaluated on a case-by-case basis, taking into consideration the requirements for responding to spills, leaks or other accidental or gradual releases of hazardous wastes into the environment.

Water at Adequate Volume and Pressure [40 CFR 265.32(d)]

The use of the term "adequate" refers to the volume and pressure necessary to properly supply water hoses, automatic sprinklers, spray systems or foam-producing equipment.

Testing and Maintenance of Equipment [40 CFR 265.33]

All of the emergency equipment required must be tested and maintained as necessary to assure its proper operation in time of emergency. Such equipment includes communication devices, alarm systems, fire protection equipment and spill control equipment. Testing and maintenance implies and requires a formal, written inspection and evaluation program for such equipment. This inspection and testing program could be performed internally, e.g., by security guards. However, there are other sources of these types of inspections. Very often, loss prevention specialists from insurance carriers will review and inspect such equipment. Local fire departments often provide similar services. There also are private firms that will routinely provide inspection, testing and maintenance services for fire extinguishers and fire control equipment. It is important to keep records of the performance of such duties, to document compliance with this requirement.

Access to Communications or Alarm System [40 CFR 265.34]

The regulations require that all personnel involved in the pouring, mixing or handling of hazardous wastes at the accumulation area(s) must have immediate access to an internal alarm or emergency communication device. As explained above, such access must be provided only if such equipment is required due to the hazards posed by the wastes handled at the facility. Also, such access can be provided through visual or voice contact with another employee, as explained earlier.

However, if such devices are to be provided at or near the accumulation area for direct use by waste-handling employees, the meaning of the term "immediate" comes into question. Obviously, if the employees have to travel more than a few steps from the accumulation area to obtain access, then the alarm or communication device is not immediately available.

Common sense holds that employees will be better able to control or limit any fires or spills or leaks when alarms, communication devices, fire extinguishers and spill absorbent are all close at hand.

This section also requires that external communication devices (telephone or hand-held two-way radio) be immediately available (if required) at the scene of operation if there is ever just one employee on the premises while the "facility" is operating. The definition of facility was discussed earlier in the chapter in regard to the orientation of the regulations to commercial (offsite) hazardous waste management facilities. For manufacturing firms, it is unclear whether this provision applies when only one employee is handling wastes, or when there is only one employee at the facility when wastes are being handled (for example, during a plant shutdown for maintenance or renovation).

Given that manufacturing firms normally have many people present, and that waste-handling operations are carried out by two or more persons during regular shifts, and that accumulation areas are usually in the approximate vicinity of plant operations and other employees, the author contends that the latter interpretation holds. However, if waste accumulation is conducted in remote areas of the plant property and normally only one worker is involved, then such immediate access to external communications should be provided along with access to internal alarm or communication systems. Again, such access is required only if the hazard(s) posed by the wastes handled could require this kind of equipment.

Required Aisle Space [40 CFR 265.35]

Adequate aisle space is required for several reasons. Aisle space is needed to inspect containers for deterioration, leakage and the accumulation start date. Adequate aisle space is necessary for easy access to the wastes, for example, when a particular type of waste is ready for offsite shipment.

This provision of the regulations requires that sufficient aisle space be maintained for emergency purposes. In other words, sufficient aisle space must be maintained "to allow the unobstructed movement of personnel, fire protection equipment, spill control equipment, and decontamination equipment to any area of 'facility' operation in an emergency, unless aisle space is not needed for any of these purposes."

Again, it is important to remember the regulatory definition of "facility" and to recognize the size differences between an accumulation area (where wastes must be moved offsite or to an onsite TSD area within 90 days from the accumulation start date) and the storage area of a TSD facility, where much larger amounts are likely to be present.

For the purposes of accumulation area compliance with required aisle space, a system of main aisles and minor aisles could be devised. The two-high-and-two-wide container placement rule of thumb still applies. A main aisle would be sufficiently wide (minimum of 5 ft) to allow access by forklifts, front-end loaders or personnel with fire equipment. Minor aisles would be sufficiently wide (minimum of 2 ft) to allow access for inspection purposes.

Arrangements with Local Authorities [40 CFR 265.37]

Arrangements with local authorities are potentially a very important element of a preparedness and prevention program. Basically, the required arrangements are to familiarize local public safety agencies with the plant layout, areas where hazardous wastes are stored and the particular hazards posed by the wastes. As with equipment requirements, arrangements with local authorities are required as appropriate for the type of waste handled at the facility and the potential need for the services of these outside organizations.

Theoretically, if a manufacturing firm did not handle ignitable or reactive wastes, or DOT flammables or combustibles, then there would be little need for arrangements with local police or fire departments. If liquid hazardous wastes are accumulated only in small quantities, then the services of an outside spill control or emergency response team may not be necessary.

Additionally, some large manufacturing plants have internal fire brigades, equipped with fire trucks and foam equipment, and trained in firefighting techniques. Such facilities may have little potential need for the services of local police and fire departments.

However, the requirements for arrangements with local authorities are not onerous, and such arrangements could promote goodwill with municipal officials and perhaps reduce insurance premiums. Many manufacturing firms are on good terms with local public safety agencies. These regulatory requirements present a good opportunity for a closer relationship and perhaps reciprocal training. In other words, the fire department would train an internal fire brigade on general firefighting techniques, in exchange for hazardous waste management training by appropriate personnel from the manufacturing firm.

If such arrangements are appropriate for the type of waste handled and there is a potential need for the services of outside emergency organizations, the generator who accumulates must attempt to make the following arrangements:

*Arrangements with Local Police Departments, Fire Departments
and Emergency Response Teams to Familiarize Them with
the Operations of the Manufacturing Firm*

These aspects include:

1. the overall layout of the manufacturing facility;
2. areas where hazardous wastes are accumulated or stored;
3. properties of the hazardous waste handled at the facility and associated hazards;
4. places where personnel would normally be working;
5. entrances to roads inside the facility; and
6. possible evacuation routes.

A few of the above items need to be expanded.

Any efforts to familiarize local officials on the plant layout and location of hazardous waste should include information on how and where hazardous input materials (such as bulk solvents or chemicals) are stored. Emergencies can occur involving raw material as well as hazardous waste handling or storage.

When discussing the properties of the hazardous materials and wastes handled and the associated hazards, it will be important to include the types of hazards associated with the conditions to which local police and fire personnel will respond. In other words, what are the hazards of spilled or leaked material when exposed to air or water? The hazards resulting from the wastes being combusted or exposed to heat or flame should also be explained. Many materials form toxic gaseous by-products under such conditions. This information would be in addition to the properties of and hazards posed by the wastes under "normal" conditions.

For the purposes of this requirement, representatives of the facility could organize group tours of the plant, distribute written material on the necessary aspects of plant operations and/or distribute copies of the facility's contingency plan. It is important to document any contacts made with local authorities, any agreements/arrangements or refusal by local authorities to enter into any formal agreements/arrangements. If tours are conducted, a list of attendees and the areas toured, along with the date(s) of the tour(s) should be prepared and kept on file.

Agreements Designating Primary Emergency Authority
to a Specific Police and a Specific Fire Department

This requirement provides the opportunity to clearly delineate responsibility when a manufacturing facility is located in overlapping jurisdictions. This could be the case in the suburbs of a large city, where township or volunteer fire departments exist in addition to the municipal fire department. Insurance premiums may be reduced if primary response authority is given to the municipal fire department, with backup support provided by the other fire departments.

Agreements with State Emergency Response Teams, Emergency Response Contractors and Equipment Suppliers

Again, these agreements are required as appropriate, given the type of waste handled and the potential need for such services. It must be stated, however, that many states have very strict spill-reporting laws. It may be advisable to at least notify the state spill response authority of the types of wastes and materials handled, and find out the specific reporting requirements. A letter to this effect to the state spill response authority will probably suffice. The state spill response authority can easily be contacted by calling the spill response number found in the telephone book. It may be that spill reporting and response functions are not organizationally located within the state hazardous waste management agency.

Arrangements to Familiarize Local Hospitals with the Properties of Hazardous Waste Handled at the Facility and the Types of Illnesses That Could Result from Fires, Explosions, Spills or Leaks at the Facility

This could be as simple as contracting with an industrial clinic to handle employee injuries. The clinic could be provided with information such as material safety data sheets or chemical literature on the types of materials and wastes handled. If a local hospital's emergency room is more convenient, similar arrangements could be made with the emergency room supervisor or hospital authorities.

With this and the other required arrangements/agreements, it is important to document the contacts made, the information transferred, any meetings, tours, etc. Refusal by local authorities should also be documented. If local authorities are particularly reluctant to enter into written agreements, then the required information could be sent to them via certified mail, return receipt requested. The signed receipt would then be attached to a photocopy of the information mailed. This documentation becomes part of the record-keeping system used to allow ready verification of compliance by regulatory officials.

CONTINGENCY PLAN AND EMERGENCY PROCEDURES
[40 CFR 265, Subpart D]

A contingency plan incorporating the procedures necessary to respond to emergencies involving hazardous waste is an important document for generators who store or accumulate. The contingency plan can be thought of as the central document of a preparedness and prevention program. In fact, the requirements of Subpart C, "Preparedness and Prevention," and Subpart D, "Contingency Plan and Emergency Procedures," are intertwined.

A contingency plan should be a concise document, a one-stop source of the basic information necessary to respond effectively to an emergency involving hazardous waste. A contingency plan should be designed and written to be useful and to be used. A good contingency plan can serve as the core of the required personnel training program. It should be posted at or near storage and accumulation areas. Copies should be given to responsible personnel at the manufacturing facility. The plan should be distributed to local emergency authorities.

The requirements for a contingency plan offer plant management and personnel assigned responsibilities for hazardous waste a unique opportunity to plan for emergency incidents at the manufacturing facility. Of course, possible incidents are not limited to those involving the firm's hazardous waste storage or accumulation areas. Incidents can involve the various hazardous materials used in the manufacturing process. A good contingency plan can be integrated into emergency planning for other incidents, such as the responses necessary to fires or explosions not involving hazardous wastes, floods, power outages, tornadoes, earthquakes, broken gas or water mains, railroad derailments, or civil disobedience.

To be useful, the persons involved in the preparation of the contingency plan should attempt to anticipate the potential types of incidents involving hazardous wastes. Appropriate responses should then be laid out for each type of incident. The more likely types of incidents include:

1. fire;
2. explosion;
3. leakage from deteriorated or damaged containers to waterways or sewers;
4. spills during routine handling;
5. splashes involving worker injury;

6. spills or leaks producing toxic vapors or fumes; and
7. contamination resulting from containers ruptured due to buildup of internal pressure.

The specific conditions at the manufacturing operation as well as the types of wastes handled may require other potential incidents to be explored. Some sorting and sifting of the less feasible incidents should be performed by assessing the potential incident in terms of the probability of occurrence and the severity of the consequences.

Personnel Actions

A description of the actions facility personnel must take in response to fires, explosions or any unplanned releases of hazardous waste or hazardous waste constituents to air, soil or surface water at the facility is the core of the contingency plan. This is where the potential incidents and appropriate responses will be laid out.

The regulations lay out a performance standard for these planned responses. The contingency plan must be designed to minimize hazards to human health or the environment from fires, explosions or any unplanned releases. Further, the provisions of the plan must be carried out immediately whenever there is a fire, explosion or release that could threaten human health or the environment.

Arrangements with Authorities

A description should be included of arrangements agreed to by local police departments, fire departments, hospitals, contractors, and state and local emergency response teams to coordinate emergency services.

These are the agreements potentially required as a part of the preparedness and prevention program. Hopefully, the agreements specify the circumstances and signal(s) necessary to activate the arrangements.

List of Emergency Coordinators

A list should be made of names, addresses and phone numbers (office and home) of all persons qualified to act as emergency coordinator. Where more than one person is listed, one person must be named as primary emergency coordinator and others must be listed in the order in which they will assume responsibility as alternates.

Emergency Coordinator

The emergency coordinator has heavy responsibilities to assume in an emergency. At least one employee capable of acting as an emergency coordinator is required at all times to either be on the facility premises or on call. The emergency coordinator has the responsibility for coordinating all emergency response measures and must have the authority to commit resources (incur debts) to carry out the contingency plan. The emergency coordinator(s) should be a highly capable and well-trained individual. Persons listed as emergency coordinators should be thoroughly familiar with and knowledgeable about:

1. all aspects of the contingency plan;
2. all operations and activities at the facility;
3. the location and characteristics of wastes handled;
4. the location of all records within the facility; and
5. the facility layout.

The emergency coordinator is required to perform certain activities and follow certain procedures in an emergency. Whenever there is an imminent or actual emergency situation:

1. The emergency coordinator (or his designee when the emergency coordinator is on call) must immediately activate internal facility alarms or communication systems to notify all facility personnel, and notify appropriate state or local agencies with designated response roles if their help is needed [265.56(a)(1) & (2)].
2. If there is a release, fire or explosion, the emergency coordinator must immediately identify the character, exact source, amount and areal extent of any released materials. This may be done by observation or review of facility records or manifests and, if necessary, by chemical analysis [265.56(b)].
3. At the same time, the emergency coordinator must assess possible hazards to human health or the environment that may result from the release, fire or explosion [265.56(c)].
4. If the emergency coordinator determines that the facility has had a release, fire or explosion that could threaten human health or the environment outside the facility, he must report his findings as follows. If his assessment indicates that evacuation of local areas may be advisable, he must immediately notify appropriate local

authorities. The emergency coordinator must be available to help appropriate officials decide whether local areas should be evacuated. He must immediately notify the National Response Center using their 24-hour toll-free number (1-800-424-8802). The report must include: (1) name and telephone number of caller; (2) name and address of facility; (3) time and type of incident (e.g., release, fire); (4) name and quantity of material(s) involved, to the extent known; (5) the extent of injuries, if any; and (6) the possible hazards to human health or the environment outside the facility [265.56(d)(1)-(2)].

5. During an emergency, the emergency coordinator must take all reasonable measures necessary to ensure that fires, explosions and releases do not occur, recur or spread to other hazardous waste at the facility. These measures must include, where applicable, stopping processes and operations, collecting and containing released waste, and removing or isolating containers [265.56(e)].

6. If the facility stops operations in response to a fire, explosion or release, the emergency coordinator must monitor for leaks, pressure buildup, gas generation or ruptures in valves, pipes or other equipment, wherever this is appropriate [265.56(f)].

7. Immediately after an emergency, the emergency coordinator must provide for treating, storing or disposing of recovered waste, contaminated soil or surface water, or any other material that results from a release, fire or explosion at a facility [265.56(g)].

8. The emergency coordinator must ensure that, in the affected area(s) of the facility: (1) no waste that may be incompatible with the released material is treated, stored or disposed of until cleanup procedures are completed; and (2) all emergency equipment listed in the contingency plan is cleaned and fit for its intended use before operations are resumed [265.56(h)].

9. The owner or operator must notify the EPA regional administrator and appropriate state and local authorities that the facility is in compliance with the previous paragraph before operations are resumed in the affected area(s) of the facility [265.56(i)].

10. The owner or operator must note in the operating record the time, date and details of any incident that requires implementing the contingency plan. Within 15 days after the incident he must submit a written report on the incident to the EPA regional administrator. The report must include: (1) name, address and telephone number of the owner or operator; (2) name, address and telephone number of the facility; (3) date, time and type of incident; (4) name and quantity of material(s) involved; (5) the extent of injuries, if any; (6) an assessment of actual or potential hazards to human health or the environment, where this is applicable; and (7) estimated quantity and disposition of recovered material that resulted from the incident [265.56(j)].

Equipment List

A list should be included of all emergency equipment at the facility, including the location and a physical description of each item on the list, and a brief outline of its capabilities.

The emergency equipment could include, where required, fire extinguishers, spill control equipment, communication and alarm systems, and decontamination equipment. The subject of required emergency equipment was discussed earlier in regard to preparedness and prevention programs.

A point of interest, once again, is the use of the term "facility" in the regulatory language. The author interprets the term "facility" to refer to the hazardous waste management facility (in this case the accumulation area) within the overall manufacturing facility. It is clearly illogical to require a listing of all emergency equipment (e.g., fire extinguishers) at a manufacturing establishment when only those extinguishers or pieces of equipment readily available could possibly be used in case of fire or emergency.

Of course, all emergency equipment that could potentially be used to respond in an emergency should be listed, whether physically located at the accumulation area ("facility") or not. For example, some manufacturing plants have internal fire brigades with mobile foam-producing firefighting equipment. Clearly, these capabilities should be included in the equipment list and in the response planning for emergencies.

Some contingency plans have implemented this requirement as a list and a plant layout map. There is a list of equipment, with a physical description and outline of the capabilities of each item separate from, but attached to a plant layout map showing the accumulation area(s). Symbols are used to show the location of the items on the list within or near the accumulation area(s).

Evacuation Plan

An evacuation plan for facility personnel should be prepared where there is a possibility that evacuation could be necessary.

Again, the term "facility" is a point of concern. Obviously, if ignitable or reactive wastes are stored inside of buildings or near where employees work, the evacuation plan should be for the entire manufacturing facility, or at least the building where wastes are accumulated. If accumulation areas are outside of or remote from areas where production employees work, the evacuation plan could focus on the evacuation of waste-handling personnel from the accumulation areas and the immediately adjacent areas.

Where an evacuation plan is necessary, it must describe the signal(s) to be used to begin evacuation, the evacuation routes, and alternate evacuation routes if there is a possibility that the primary routes could be blocked by fires or releases of hazardous wastes.

Additional Considerations

EPA has prepared a guidance manual that covers, among other things, the preparation of contingency plans. Entitled "Plans, Record-keeping, Variances, and Demonstrations for Hazardous Waste Treatment, Storage, and Disposal Facilities" (SW-921), this manual presents a suggested outline of some merit for contingency plans. This suggested outline is found in Table V.

As mentioned earlier, the potential types of incidents should have appropriate responses laid out. This is the essence of the contingency plan. For each incident, a series of steps should be devised to adequately respond. Also, the equipment, materials and personnel protection (e.g., respirators and protective clothing) necessary to respond to each incident should be identified. The response strategy should specify when to invoke the arrangements/agreements with state and local authorities, and decision criteria for evacuation. Not to be overlooked are decision criteria for contingency plan implementation. Example contingency plan implementation criteria (from SW-921) are found in Table VI.

Once the contingency plan is implemented, the emergency coordinator has little latitude regarding certain actions. Section 265.56 specifies in some detail the emergency procedures the emergency coordinator must follow. The requirements of Section 265.56, "Emergency Procedures," were given earlier in this chapter. The procedures to be followed can be divided into three phases: (1) discovery and notification phase; (2) containment and control phase; and (3) followup and cleanup phase. A sample emergency procedures checklist (from SW-921) incorporating these three phases is given in Table VII. This checklist references certain elements of the facility contingency plan by page number. The requirements of Section 265.56 should be extensively referenced in any contingency plan developed, because of their specificity and mandatory nature.

Table V.   Suggested Outline of Contingency Plan[a]

Facility Identification and General Information
1. Name of facility
2. Location
3. Name, address and telephone numbers (office and home) of owner and operator
4. Name, title, address and telephone numbers (office and home) of primary emergency coordinator and alternates
5. Type of facility
6. Facility site plan (including structures, topography, roadways, sewers, pipelines or utility networks, adjacent land uses and water bodies)
7. Description of hazardous waste activities (including types of wastes, amounts and capacities)

Emergency Coordinator(s)
1. Primary coordinator
2. Alternate coordinator(s)
3. Emergency duties and authority to commit resources

Implementation of Contingency Plan
1. Decision criteria for each potential type of incident
2. Decision criteria for calling for outside assistance

Emergency Response Procedures
1. Notification phase
2. Control and containment phase
3. Followup and cleanup phase

Emergency Equipment
1. Emergency equipment inventory
2. Location of emergency equipment
3. Equipment capabilities
4. Emergency equipment available from other sources

Coordination Agreements
1. Police
2. Fire
3. Other emergency response units
4. Hospital

Evacuation Plan
1. When to evacuate
2. Signals to begin evacuation
3. Primary evacuation routes
4. Alternate evacuation routes

Required Reports
1. Notification of compliance before resuming operations following incident
2. Report on the incident

Identification of Hazardous Materials
1. Material safety data sheets
2. Other reference materials on chemicals present

---

[a]Modified from "Plans, Recordkeeping, Variances, and Demonstrations for Hazardous Waste Treatment, Storage, and Disposal Facilities," SW-921, U.S. EPA, U.S. Government Printing Office (1981), pp. 45-46.

Table VI.   Example Contingency Plan Implementation Criteria[a]

The contingency plan must be implemented if an imminent or actual incident could threaten the environment or human health

Spills

The spill could result in release of flammable liquids or vapors, creating a fire or gas explosion hazard

The spill could cause the release of toxic liquids or fumes

The spill can be contained onsite, but the potential exists for groundwater pollution due to aquifer contamination

The spill cannot be contained onsite, resulting in offsite soil contamination and/or ground- or surface-water pollution.

Fires

The fire could cause the release of toxic fumes

If the fire spreads, it could ignite materials at other locations at the site or cause heat-induced explosions

The fire could spread to offsite areas

Use of water or water and chemical fire suppressant could result in contaminated runoff

Explosions

An imminent danger exists that an explosion could occur, resulting in a safety hazard due to flying fragments or shock waves

An imminent danger exists that an explosion could ignite other hazardous waste at the facility

An imminent danger exists that an explosion could result in release of toxic material

An explosion has occurred

---

[a]From "Plans, Recordkeeping, Variances, and Demonstrations for Hazardous Waste Treatment, Storage, and Disposal Facilities," SW-921, U.S. EPA, U.S. Government Printing Office (1981), p. 48.

The contingency plan is not meant to be a static document. The contingency plan must be reviewed and amended immediately if necessary, whenever:

1. applicable regulations are revised;
2. the plan fails in an emergency;
3. the facility changes in a way that materially increases the potential for incidents or changes the responses necessary to emergencies;
4. the list of emergency coordinators changes; or
5. the list of emergency equipment changes [265.54(a)-(e)].

Table VII.   Sample Emergency Procedures Checklist[a]

Immediately on discovery of an imminent or actual emergency, the emergency coordinator must:

1. Activate the internal alarm or communication system to notify facility personnel.
   - Are all personnel accounted for?
   - Are there any injuries?
2. Notify state or local agencies with designated response roles if their help is needed.
   - Can facility personnel control the emergency?
   ° Emergency response phone numbers: page _____
3. Notify EPA on-scene coordinator or National Response Center of incident.
   ° Emergency response phone numbers: page _____
4. Identify character, exact source, amount and areal extent of any released material.
   - Is facility evacuation necessary?
   ° Identification of hazardous materials: Appendix _____
   ° Facility evacuation plan: page _____
5. Assess hazards to the environment and human health.
6. Determine if evacuation of local area is advisable. If so, notify local authorities.
   - Will prevailing winds carry toxic fumes toward populated areas?
   - Is explosion likely?

During the emergency control phase, the emergency coordinator must:

1. Ensure that proper and adequate measures are taken to respond to the incident. If necessary, commit facility resources and incur debts to properly respond.
2. Take measures to ensure the incident does not recur or spread to other hazardous waste at the facility. Shut down operations if necessary.
   ° Emergency response measures: page _____
3. Monitor equipment for leaks, pressure buildup or other potential problems if operations are shut down.

Following attainment of control, the emergency coordinator must:

1. Provide for treating, storing or disposing of recovered waste, contaminated soil, surface water or other material resulting from the discharge.
   ° Decontamination and cleanup: page _____
2. Ensure that cleanup procedures are completed and emergency equipment is fit for use before resuming operations of affected areas.
   ° Decontamination and cleanup: page _____
3. Notify EPA, state and local officials that the facility is in compliance before resuming operation.
4. Place summary of incident (time, date and details) in operating record.
5. Submit written report on the incident to EPA regional administrator and state regulatory authorities within 15 days of the incident.

[a]Modified from "Plans, Recordkeeping, Variances, and Demonstrations for Hazardous Waste Treatment, Storage, and Disposal Facilities," SW-921, U.S. EPA, U.S. Government Printing Office (1981), pp. 50-51.

Copies of the contingency plan and all revisions must, of course, be maintained at the facility. In addition, the plan and all revisions must be submitted to the following organizations that may be called on to provide emergency services:

1.   local police departments;

2. local fire departments;
3. hospitals; and
4. state and local emergency response teams.

It is necessary to note that any existing spill prevention, control and countermeasures (SPCC) plans prepared to comply with Clean Water Act regulations [40 CFR 112 or 1510] can be amended to meet the contingency plan requirements. SPCC plans need to be amended to incorporate the five elements of a contingency plan discussed above.

Conclusion

It is important to note the existence of parallel federal, state and, often, local requirements for reporting spills and other emergency incidents. The various laws and regulations at the different levels of government have different specifications as to what, where and how much constitutes a reportable incident. The hazardous waste regulations (under RCRA) require reporting to the National Response Center (1-800-424-8802) if there is a release, fire or explosion that could threaten human health or the environment outside the facility. The applicable Clean Water Act regulations [40 CFR 117] focus on the discharge of "reportable quantities" of hazardous substances [40 CFR 116] into the waters of the United States. The term "waters of the United States" is very broadly interpreted. The U.S. government (via the National Response Center) must be notified of the discharge of hazardous substances in quantities equal to or exceeding the reportable quantity (specified in 40 CFR 117 for each hazardous substance) over any 24-hr period. The Comprehensive Environmental Response, Compensation and Liability Act (CERCLA) of 1980 ("Superfund") uses the "release" concept. A "release" is defined to include spills and practically all other methods by which a pollutant may reach the environment. Releases of "hazardous substances" (designated under the Clean Water Act, Clean Air Act, RCRA and the Toxic Substances Control Act) to the environment in reportable quantities must be reported to the National Response Center.

It is important that the contingency plan address the various spill and emergency incident reporting requirements. Inquiries should be made to the following agencies as to their reporting requirements for emergency incidents and accidental discharges, releases or spills:

1. state air pollution control agency;
2. state water pollution control agency;

3.   state solid/hazardous waste management agency;
4.   state fire marshal's office;
5.   municipal sewage treatment authority;
6.   municipal water supply authority;
7.   municipal public works authority;
8.   local air pollution control agency;
9.   local civil defense or emergency management agency.

The emergency procedures developed for the contingency plan should include the reporting requirements of the various governmental agencies. Waste-handling employees should be trained to report all spills to a designated employee, who will be responsible for contacting the necessary agencies.

PERSONNEL TRAINING [40 CFR 265.16]

The final requirement of Section 262.34 for generators who accumulate is that of a personnel training program. Employees directly involved with waste management and handling must successfully complete a program of instruction that teaches them to properly perform their duties. This training program can consist of classroom instruction, on-the-job training or some combination of the two. However, the training program and the training that each individual receives must meet a very broad performance standard. The performance standard specified in the regulations is this: the training program must teach the employees required to take it to perform their duties in a way that ensures the facility's compliance with the Part 265 standards.

The regulations do give some guidance as to what constitutes the minimally acceptable personnel training program. At a minimum, the training program is to ensure that waste-handling employees are able to respond effectively to emergencies. This is to be done by familiarizing such employees

with emergency procedures, emergency equipment, and emergency systems, including where applicable:

(i) Procedures for using, inspecting, repairing, and replacing facility emergency and monitoring equipment;
(ii) Key parameters for automatic waste feed cut-off systems;
(iii) Communications or alarm systems;
(iv) Response to fires or explosions;

(v) Response to ground-water contamination incidents;
(vi) Shutdown of operations [40 CFR 265.16(a)(3)].

The minimal guidance given in the regulations is not, in the author's opinion, sufficient to meet the regulatory performance standard. Employees with waste management duties need to be trained in more than emergency procedures if they are going to operate the facility in compliance with the interim status standards found in Part 265. Employees should be trained to be able to handle hazardous wastes in a manner that will minimize the possibility of fire, explosion or release. Most firms will also want their training program to ensure that the appropriate employees will be able to ensure the firm's compliance with the standards found in 40 CFR 261 and 262.

A good training program would begin with instruction on safe handling of hazardous wastes under normal conditions. This program could include use of the SOP, the development of which is discussed in Chapter 16. The goal of such a program would be to maintain compliance under both normal operating conditions and during emergency situations. This can only be achieved by training in both proper operating procedures and emergency response measures.

It is very likely that several people at a typical manufacturing firm will, due to their involvement in waste management, need to complete successfully the training program. These people will likely have different duties and levels of responsibility. The training program should be structured for the differing information and training needs of the different types of positions involved in HWM. Waste management employees should receive instruction on HWM procedures (including contingency plan implementation) relevant to the duties and responsibilities of the positions in which they are employed. The training program is to be directed by a person already trained in hazardous waste management procedures.

This training was to have been successfully completed by the relevant employees by May 19, 1981. New employees or employees reassigned to waste management duties are to complete the training program within six months after the date of employment or reassignment. Such employees are not to work in unsupervised positions until they have successfully completed the training program. Successful completion may be documented by having the trainees take a written test. Finally, all employees falling under the training requirement must take part in an annual review of the initial training.

As with many of the other requirements, the training program must be well documented and dutifully recorded. The following documents and records should be considered an integral part of the training program:

1. the job title for each position at the facility related to HWM and the name of the employee filling each job;
2. a written job description for each position at the facility related to HWM, including the requisite skill, education or other qualifications, and duties of employees assigned to each position;
3. a written description of the type and amount of introductory and continuing training that will be given each person filling a position at the facility related to HWM; and
4. records that document that the required training has been given to and completed by each person filling a position related to HWM.

Once a curriculum is devised that would meet the requirements of the regulations, the training could be implemented as a series of topics. Topics could include use of fire extinguishers, control of minor spills/leaks, how to conduct inspections of storage areas, handling considerations for each of the facility's waste streams, etc. An outline would be prepared for each topic. When the topic is presented to the relevant employees, the documentation would include a sign-up sheet of all attending. This sheet would include the topic of the session, the date, place, instructor and length of the course. A simple true/false or multiple-choice test may be given to document successful completion of each session. This information would be kept as part of the personnel training records.

Any instruction in emergency procedures should include implementation of the contingency plan, which would serve as an instruction manual. Perhaps a select crew of personnel could be recruited for each shift to be intensively trained in contingency plan implementation. Of course, any such crews would be supervised and coordinated by the emergency coordinator during any incident requiring implementation of the contingency plan.

CONCLUSION

The regulatory requirements for manufacturing firms as accumulators of hazardous waste are fairly comprehensive. Compliance with these requirements is much more involved than merely moving wastes offsite every 90 days. Compliance will require the implementation of a formal HWM program. Although the requirements for such a program for accumulators are not as extensive as those for storers (discussed in Chapter 11), many of the elements of such a program are shared. Setting up a compliance program is discussed in Section 3 of this book.

GENERATORS WHO STORE HAZARDOUS WASTES UNDER INTERIM STATUS

John Thomas Fitch

Land Pollution Control Division
Indiana State Board of Health
Indianapolis, Indiana

Gary F. Lindgren

Ulrich Chemical, Inc.
Indianapolis, Indiana

This chapter is devoted to manufacturing firms with an interim status storage facility on their premises. This chapter covers the hazardous waste storage practices of the great majority of manufacturing firms, i.e., storage in containers and/or tanks. The use of surface impoundments or waste piles for storage of hazardous wastes is not addressed. This chapter is intended to serve as an introduction to and reiteration of the interim status standards (ISS) applicable to storage in containers and tanks. It is not intended, however, to substitute for a close reading of the actual regulatory sections by persons responsible for waste management at manufacturing facilities. Some of the standards applicable to interim status storage facilities have been covered in Chapter 10, as they apply to accumulation areas. The reader will be advised to refer to Chapter 10 for further discussion of some topics.

The regulatory definition of storage, found in Section 260.10, is as follows:

> the holding of hazardous waste for a temporary period, at the end of which the hazardous waste is treated, disposed of, or stored elsewhere.

As discussed in Chapter 10, certain storage practices do not require a permit. These practices are primarily the accumulation of hazardous wastes for periods of time under 90 days, provided such wastes are managed at an onsite recycling facility, an onsite interim status storage facility or an offsite treatment, storage or disposal (TSD) facility. It must be remembered that even though the permit requirements apply only to storage facilities where wastes are held longer than 90 days, certain interim status standards apply to both accumulation areas and storage facilities.

The interim status standards found at 40 CFR 265 are divided into subparts and sections. Overall, however, the Part 265 standards can be categorized into those applicable to all facilities and those applicable only to a particular type of facility. The subparts generally and specifically applicable to storage facilities are:

- A: General
- B: General Facility Standards
- C: Preparedness and Prevention
- D: Contingency Plan and Emergency Procedures
- E: Manifest System, Recordkeeping, and Reporting
- G: Closure and Post-closure
- H: Financial Requirements
- I: Use and Management of Containers
- J: Tanks

Subparts A–E, G and H are generally applicable to the hazardous waste storage facilities covered in this chapter, i.e., container storage facilities and tank storage facilities. Subpart I, "Use and Management of Containers," is specifically applicable to facilities using drums or barrels or other portable storage devices in which to store or transport hazardous wastes. Subpart J, "Tanks," is specifically applicable to facilities using stationary devices constructed of nonearthen materials to contain and store hazardous wastes.

SUBPART A: GENERAL

Subpart A primarily states to whom the requirements of Part 265 do and do not apply. The standards apply to owners and operators of TSD facilities that have met the requirements for interim status. The concept of and requirements for interim status were discussed in Chapter 5. The Part 265 standards apply until final administrative disposition of Parts A and B of the permit application is made. If a permit is granted, the Part 265 standards no longer apply, as they are replaced by the 40 CFR 264 permanent status standards. If a permit is denied, the hazardous waste management facility is to close. For manufacturing firms with storage facilities, this would require hazardous wastes to be moved offsite every 90 days to a TSD facility under interim status or possessing a Resource Conservation and Recovery Act (RCRA) permit. The interesting exclusions given from the requirements of Part 265 are discussed in Chapter 13.

Subpart A has one other provision worth noting. Section 265.4, "Imminent Hazard Action," states that "Notwithstanding any other provisions of these regulations, enforcement actions may be brought pursuant to Section 7003 of RCRA." The implication is that compliance with all applicable Part 265 standards is not sufficient to prevent enforcement actions brought under the imminent hazard provisions of RCRA.

SUBPART B: GENERAL FACILITY STANDARDS

Subpart B standards encompass a wide range of subjects not readily categorized elsewhere. The owner or operator of every hazardous waste management facility subject to Part 265 must apply for a U.S. Environmental Protection Agency (EPA) identification number [265.11]. Also, before ownership or operation of a hazardous waste facility can be transferred during its operating life, the new owner or operator must be notified in writing of the requirements governing the facility as set forth in 40 CFR 122 and 265. This notification is to be made by the existing owner or operator [265.12].

These requirements, as well as the other Part 265 standards, apply to the owner of the facility, the operator of the facility or both. The regulations specify their applicability to an owner/operator for enforcement purposes. This specification of applicability is not necessary for explanatory purposes, so the remainder of the chapter will treat the requirements as if they apply to the facility itself.

General Waste Analysis [40 CFR 265.13]

Before any hazardous waste is placed in storage, a detailed chemical and physical analysis of a representative sample of the waste must be obtained. There should be an analysis of each waste in storage, giving all the information that must be known to store the waste in accordance with the Part 265 requirements. This analysis may consist of a laboratory analysis, and can include published or documented data concerning the waste in question. This waste analysis must be repeated when the process or operation that generates the waste is changed or when different input materials or chemicals are used, if such changes would modify the physical or chemical characteristics of the waste. The analysis of each waste must be repeated as necessary to ensure that it is accurate and up to date. Offsite (commercial) hazardous waste management facilities may require additional analyses, or may themselves perform analyses for information necessary to properly treat or dispose of the waste.

A written waste analysis plan is to be developed to serve as a guide to the detailed chemical and physical analyses to be performed. There are four elements of a waste analysis plan that apply to the container or tank storage facilities of manufacturing firms. The plan must specify the sampling procedure to be used to obtain a representative sample of the waste. The sampling procedure chosen depends on the physical state of the waste and the place from which it is to be sampled. The sampling procedure can be one of the methods described in Appendix I of 40 CFR 261, or an equivalent sampling method. The plan must designate the parameters for which each waste will be analyzed. The rationale for selection of these parameters (and presumably why others were not selected) must be explained, for each waste.

An explanation of how an analysis for the chosen parameters will adequately supply the information necessary for safe and proper storage of each hazardous waste should also be provided. The waste analysis plan must also specify the test methods that will be used to test for the parameters selected. The test methods for the characteristics of a hazardous waste [ignitability, corrosivity or extraction procedure (EP) toxicity] should be those mandated by the regulations. Appendix III of 40 CFR 261 specifies appropriate analytical procedures and approved measurement techniques for various organic chemicals and inorganic species. Further guidance on acceptable and approved methods and procedures can be found in "Test Methods for Evaluating Solid Waste: Physical/Chemical Methods" (SW-846), U.S. EPA (1980). If the services of a commercial laboratory are used, the laboratory personnel may be of some service in identifying appropriate test methods for each parameter for each waste. Finally, the waste analysis plan must specify the frequency with which the initial analysis of each waste will be reviewed or repeated to ensure that the analysis is accurate and up to date.

Waste Management Facility Security [40 CFR 265.14]

Security provisions are necessary to prevent unknowing or unauthorized entry to the facility. A facility must have (1) a 24-hr surveillance system (e.g., television monitoring or surveillance by guards) that monitors and controls entry, or (2) a natural or artificial barrier that surrounds the facility (e.g., a fence). If a fence is used, there must be a means of controlling access at all times through the gate, such as a lock, an attendant or a guard.

Manufacturing firms generally meet this requirement by a fence surrounding the entire plant property. Any gates or entryways must be locked or monitored. At each entrance to the facility and at other locations near the actual storage area, signs must be posted displaying the legend "Danger—Unauthorized Personnel Keep Out."

General Inspection Requirements [40 CFR 265.15]

The storage facility is to be inspected periodically for malfunctions, deterioration, operator errors and discharges that may cause release of hazardous waste or constituents thereof to the environment, or a threat to human health. These inspections must be conducted often enough to identify problems and correct them before any releases to the environment or damage to human health.

As with the waste analysis requirements, the inspection requirements begin with a written procedure. In this case, the procedure is called an inspection schedule, rather than a plan. The inspection schedule applies to all monitoring equipment, safety and emergency equipment, security devices, and operating and structural equipment (e.g., dikes and sump pumps) that are required by regulation or that are important to preventing, detecting or responding to environmental or human health hazards.

The inspection schedule must identify the types of problems to be looked for during the inspection. A specification of the frequency of inspection for each item on the schedule is required. The frequency of inspection is a decision made by the operator. However, this discretion is limited. Loading and unloading areas, and other areas subject to spills must be inspected daily when in use. Further, the inspection schedule must include the items and frequencies specified in Subpart I, "Use and Management of Containers," and Subpart J, "Tanks." Container storage areas must be inspected at least weekly and tank storage areas must be inspected daily for some items and weekly for others. For all other items, the inspection frequency should be based on a consideration of both the rate of possible deterioration and the probability of an environmental or human health incident if the deterioration or malfunction or error goes undetected.

Merely performing inspections according to the schedule and noting deficiencies is not sufficient. Deterioration must be remedied, malfunctions corrected and errors or bad practices stopped before an environmental or human health hazard results. Where a hazard is imminent or has already occurred, remedial action must be taken immediately. Otherwise, corrections must take place in a timely manner as stated above. Some notation of the time frame available to correct the problem should be indicated on the inspection form.

As with many other requirements, the performance of inspections must be documented. The inspections must be recorded in an inspection log or summary. These records must include:

1.   the date and time of the inspection;
2.   the name of the inspector;
3.   a notation of the observations made; and
4.   the date and nature of any repairs or other remedial actions.

These records must be kept for at least three years from the date of inspection. The inspection log requirement can be met by keeping the completed inspection forms in a three-ring binder. Otherwise, the results of the inspections can be summarized and transferred to a master log book. Many facilities have implemented the inspection requirements by developing a set of inspection forms, one form for each type of equipment for which inspection is mandated.

A good inspection schedule and regular inspections are important management tools at a hazardous waste facility. Minor problems associated with the operation of the site are found before they develop into major problems, allowing corrective actions to be initiated quickly.

Personnel Training [40 CFR 265.16]

Personnel training is one of the most critical aspects of the proper management of a hazardous waste facility. Employees must be trained so that they understand the hazardous properties of the wastes they are handling, know how to perform their routine waste management tasks, and what to do in responding to an emergency situation. Personnel training is covered in Chapter 10, as it is also a requirement for generators who accumulate.

General Requirements for Ignitable, Reactive or Incompatible Wastes [40 CFR 265.17]

Precautions are mandated at facilities handling ignitable or reactive wastes to prevent accidental ignition or reaction. Mandated precautions include separation and protection of such wastes from sources of ignition or reaction including but not limited to:

1. open flames;
2. smoking;
3. cutting and welding;
4. hot surfaces;
5. frictional heat;
6. sparks (static, electrical or mechanical);
7. spontaneous ignition; and
8. radiant heat.

Ignitable and reactive wastes should be stored in areas where smoking is prohibited. "No Smoking" signs must be posted wherever there is a hazard from ignitable or reactive waste. Finally, smoking and open flame must be confined to designated locations while ignitable or reactive wastes are being handled.

Section 265.17 also gives a performance standard for TSD of ignitable or reactive wastes, and for mixtures of incompatible wastes, or incompatible wastes and materials. Such operations must be carried out so that they do not:

1. generate extreme heat, pressure, fire, explosion or violent reaction;
2. produce uncontrolled toxic mists, fumes, dusts or gases in sufficient quantities to threaten human health;
3. produce uncontrolled flammable fumes or gases in sufficient quantities to pose a risk of fire or explosions;
4. damage the structural integrity of the device or facility containing the waste; or
5. through other like means threaten the environment.

To adequately address these requirements for ignitable, reactive and incompatible wastes, the generator must first know the properties of the wastes in storage, and must determine (in laboratory trial tests) the results of subjecting the wastes to various conditions likely encountered in storage (extreme heat, freezing, precipitation and rough handling). The generator should also determine whether any two waste types are incompatible. Only with such information can the regulatory requirements be addressed and the wastes protected adequately.

Subparts I and J of 40 CFR 265 give more specific instruction with respect to the management of ignitable, reactive and incompatible wastes. Discussion of such requirements as they apply to container storage areas is found in Chapter 10.

SUBPART C: PREPAREDNESS AND PREVENTION

A preparedness and prevention program is an important requirement of storage facilities as well as of accumulation areas. The regulations specify a performance standard in this regard: that the storage facility be maintained and operated to minimize the possibility of fire, explosion, or unplanned sudden or gradual release of hazardous waste or hazardous waste constituents to the air, soil or surface water. Preparedness and prevention programs are given extensive coverage in Chapter 10.

SUBPART D: CONTINGENCY PLAN
AND EMERGENCY PROCEDURES

The contingency plan for the storage facility is one of the most important documents to be developed. The contingency plan should address potential emergency situations involving hazardous wastes. For each situation there should be a complete, organized and considered response that will adequately manage the situation. The requirements of Subpart D are thoroughly discussed in Chapter 10.

SUBPART E: MANIFEST SYSTEM,
RECORD-KEEPING AND REPORTING

Subpart E applies to onsite storage facilities of manufacturing firms only with regard to record-keeping and reporting requirements. The manifest system requirements found in Subpart E apply only to commercial offsite TSD facilities, and do not apply to onsite facilities that do not receive any hazardous wastes from offsite sources. The manifest system requirements applicable to manufacturing firms generating and storing hazardous waste are found at 40 CFR Part 262, and are discussed in Chapter 12.

The major requirement of Subpart E with respect to storage facilities is that of an operating record. The operating record, as the name implies, consists of a set of documents associated with the operation of the hazardous waste management facility. The operating record need not be in a single book or binder. It can be devised as a series of three ring binders, which can be kept at different locations onsite. The following information must be recorded and maintained in the operating record until closure of the storage facility:

1. a description and the quantity of each hazardous waste stored, and the method and date of its storage at the facility;
2. the location of each hazardous waste within the facility and the quantity at each location;
3. records and results of waste analyses and trial tests performed;
4. summary reports and details of all incidents (if any) that required implementation of the contingency plan, as specified in Section 265.56(j);
5. records and results of inspections as required by Section 265.15(d) (except these need only be kept for three years);
6. all closure cost estimates as required by Section 265.142; and
7. documentation of any refusal by local authorities to enter into emergency agreements.

Elements 3–7 of an operating record are fairly simple. However, some further explanation of elements 1 and 2 above is necessary, since the regulations do not specify a format for the required information. The requirements of elements 1 and 2 can be met in a variety of ways. It is important to note that these are not static requirements, but must be revised as wastes are placed in storage or shipped offsite for treatment or disposal.

One means by which the requirements of operating record element 1 can be implemented is by use of an operating log of the format shown in Table VIII. Element 1 consists of four different information needs. They are: (1) description of the waste; (2) quantity of the waste; (3) method(s) of handling; and (4) date(s) of handling. Appendix I of 40 CFR 265 provides additional guidance on meeting these information needs.

The description of the waste must include its common name, the

Table VIII.   Operating Log

For the Period Starting_____

　　　　　　　Ending_____

Common Name
Process Generating the Waste
EPA Hazardous Waste Number(s)
Physical State[a]
Quantity[b]
Method of Storage
Container Storage Area or Tank Number
Date of Storage
Date of Shipment
Disposal Firm
Manifest Number
Date Manifest Returned

[a]Solid, liquid or sludge.
[b]Weight or volume and density.

EPA hazardous waste number(s) that applies to the waste, and the physical state of the waste (solid, liquid or sludge). For characteristic hazardous wastes, the description must also include the process generating the waste. Where the waste contains more than one listed hazardous waste, or where more than one hazardous waste characteristic applies, the waste description must include all applicable EPA hazardous waste numbers.

The quantity of each hazardous waste placed in storage must also be known. The estimated or measured weight, or volume and density (where applicable) can be used. The units of measure must be shown, using the units and symbols specified in Table 1 of Appendix I of 40 CFR 265, which are:

- Mass
    - pounds: P
    - short tons (2000 lb): T
    - kilograms: K
    - metric tons (1000 kg): M
- Volume
    - gallons (U.S.): G
    - liters: L
    - cubic yards: Y
    - cubic meters: C
- Density
    - pounds/gallon: P/G

tons/cubic yard: T/Y
kilograms/liter: K/L
metric tons/cubic meter: M/C

Finally, element 1 requires the method(s) and date(s) of storage to be recorded. Table 2 of Appendix I of 40 CFR 265 specifies the handling codes to be used. For storage facilities, the only codes of interest are:

- SO1: container (barrel, drum, etc.) storage,
- SO2: tank storage,
- SO3: waste pile,
- SO4: surface impoundment, and
- SO5: other (specify).

The second element of an operating record is not quite as complex. The location of each waste within the facility and the quantity at each location must be known. A map of the storage facility using a grid system could be devised. For relatively small facilities, each block of the grid would represent one drum. Tanks would be numbered individually, of course. This information would be cross-referenced with the operating log. This map would have to indicate whether a specific block was being occupied or not, so the map would have to be updated as wastes are moved in, and a new map developed each time a shipment of wastes is taken offsite.

Availability, Retention and Disposition of Records [40 CFR 265.74]

All records, including plans, required under Part 265 must be available at all reasonable times for inspection at the facility by duly designated federal or state inspectors. Such records and plans must be furnished on request. The retention period for records required under Part 265 is automatically extended by any unresolved enforcement actions or as requested by the federal or state regulatory agencies.

As might be expected, keeping of records is inevitably accompanied by submission of reports. Storage facilities at manufacturing firms potentially have four different types of reports to submit. They are:

1. annual reports;
2. reports of incidents requiring implementation of the contingency plan;

3.   certification of closure; and
4.   exception reports.

Exception reports deal with manifest copies not returned by an offsite TSD and are discussed in Chapter 12. Closure procedures are discussed later in this chapter. The contingency plan was discussed in Chapter 10.

The annual report is a requirement of generators as well as of TSD facilities. A manufacturing firm generating hazardous wastes and storing such wastes at an onsite interim status facility would have to fill out two annual report forms. EPA suspended the annual report requirement for calendar year 1980 for generators and TSD facilities [46 FR 8395]. EPA delayed the calendar year 1981 annual report requirements with the intention of eliminating such reporting requirements of all facilities, instead substituting an annual survey of a selected sample of generators and TSD facilities [46 FR 39426 and 47 FR 7841].

It is important to note that many states have annual report requirements that apply regardless of the decision made by EPA on federal annual reports. State annual report forms may be different than the federal form found in Appendix II of 40 CFR 265.

SUBPART F: GROUNDWATER MONITORING

This subpart does not apply to facilities that store in containers or tanks. The requirements of this subpart apply to surface impoundments, landfills and land treatment facilities.

SUBPART G: CLOSURE AND POSTCLOSURE

Subpart G, as it applies to the storage facilities of manufacturing firms, requires the preparation of closure plans and mandates certain administrative procedures to be followed on closure. These requirements may seem unnecessary, as most manufacturing facilities have no intention of moving or going out of business. However, in the real world, permits are denied, storage areas are relocated within the overall plant property, plants are sold or closed, and companies go out of business. A closure plan is necessary for all these reasons.

Closure, for regulatory purposes, is the period between the last date that wastes are periodically placed in a storage facility and the submittal of a certification of completion of closure in accordance with an approved closure plan. The regulations specify a performance standard for closure: that the storage facility be closed so as to minimize post-closure environmental contamination, and that such closure should minimize the need for further maintenance. Additionally, when closure is completed, all facility equipment and structures must either be decontaminated by removing all hazardous waste and residues, or be disposed of properly.

The central document of the Subpart G requirements is the closure plan. The closure plan is to "identify the steps necessary to completely or partially close the facility at any point during its intended operating life and to completely close the facility at the end of its intended operating life" [40 CFR 265.112(a)]. As with other required documents, records and plans, the closure plan consists of a set of elements:

1. A description must be included of how and when the facility will be closed. If partial closure is applicable (e.g., the use of certain tanks in a tank storage yard will be phased out), then the description of such partial closure activities should be included. The description must identify the maximum extent of operation that will be unclosed during the life of the facility. Finally, the description must tell how the closure performance standard, the closure time periods, the decontamination of equipment requirement and the certification of closure requirement will be met.
2. An estimate must be made of the maximum inventory of wastes in storage at any time during the life of the facility.
3. A description must be given of the steps needed to decontaminate facility equipment during closure.
4. An estimate must be made of the expected year of closure and a schedule for final closure prepared.

The regulatory language with respect to closure plans makes such plans appear much more complex and harder to prepare than they really are. For container and tank storage facilities, planning for closure is actually quite simple. Basically, closure of container storage facilities will take place by removal of all containers for offsite treatment/disposal. Paved areas subject to spills will be steam-cleaned. If the container storage area is on dirt or gravel, any contaminated soil will be excavated and removed. Any sumps or catch basins used to collect spills, leaks or contaminated runoff will be emptied and cleaned. Storage facilities using tanks will have the tanks emptied and the contents managed offsite. The tanks, pumps, piping, valves, sumps, etc., will then be cleaned, and the rinsate managed properly.

Some further comments on the required elements of the closure plan are in order. Element 2 (the estimate of maximum inventory in storage) is simply the number of barrels (or the capacity of tanks used to store hazardous wastes) specified as the process design capacity in the Part A permit application. If the capacity specified in the Part A is exceeded, then both the closure plan and the Part A need to be revised. If the capacity specified in the Part A is too high, it should be revised downward, as the capacity/maximum inventory will affect the closure cost estimate and thus the amount of financial assurance necessary for closure.

Element 4 (expected year of closure) could be designated as the year the manufacturing facility is scheduled to be closed. If a new hazardous waste storage building or pad is scheduled to be built, the year of completion of the new facility could be designated as the year of closure of the existing storage area.

A schedule for final closure is also required under element 4. However, Section 265.113 of Subpart G gives certain time limitations on closure activities. Within 90 days after placing the final volume of hazardous waste in storage, or 90 days after approval of the closure plan (whichever is later) all hazardous wastes must be removed from the storage facility, in accordance with the approved closure plan. Completion of closure activities (i.e., decontamination) in accordance with the approved closure plan must take place within 180 days after receiving the final volume of wastes or 180 days after approval of the closure plan (whichever is later).

The schedule for final closure must, within these time limitations, specify the total time required to close the facility and the time required for intervening closure activities, which will allow tracking of the progress of closure. Intervening activities include removal of all wastes, decontamination of equipment and removal of contaminated soil.

The closure plan may be amended at any time during the active life of the facility (i.e., the period during which wastes are periodically placed in storage). The closure plan must be amended whenever changes in operations or facility design affect closure, or when there is a change in the expected year of closure. The plan must be amended within 60 days of such changes.

The Subpart G closure requirements also include certain administrative procedures for closure. The closure plan must be submitted to the EPA regional administrator and/or the state environmental agency at least 180 days before the expected closure date. Enforcement actions mandating closure require submission of the plan within 15 days of any closure decrees.

The federal or state regulatory agency will approve, modify or disapprove the plan within 90 days of receipt. During this period, a newspaper notice will provide the public with an opportunity to submit written comments on and request modifications of the plan. A public hearing may be held on the closure plan. If the plan is disapproved, the plan must be modified and resubmitted within 30 days. The regulatory agency must approve or modify this second plan within 60 days. If this plan is modified by the regulatory agency, it then becomes the approved closure plan. A copy of this modified closure plan is to be mailed to the owner/operator of the facility.

Once the closure plan is approved by the regulatory authorities, the closure time clock begins. As stated earlier, all waste must be removed from the facility in accordance with the closure plan within 90 days. Within 180 days, closure activities are to be completed. The facility is not officially closed until the owner/operator and an independent registered professional engineer submit certification that the facility has been closed in accordance with the approved closure plan.

SUBPART H: FINANCIAL REQUIREMENTS

Manufacturing firms with onsite container or tank storage facilities are required to be financially responsible for the closure costs and potential liabilities associated with such facilities. There are two elements to financial responsibility for such facilities: (1) assurance of sufficient funding to properly close the storage facility in accordance with the closure plan; and (2) maintenance of liability insurance to demonstrate responsibility for claims to compensate any injuries to people or property resulting from operation of the facility. Liability insurance is only required for any sudden and accidental occurrences (fires, explosions or spills) that result from operation of the facility.

Disposal facilities and facilities where wastes are to remain after closure must also have a postclosure plan and provide funds for postclosure monitoring and maintenance. Surface impoundments, landfills and land treatment facilities must demonstrate financial responsibility for claims for nonsudden occurrences (e.g., groundwater contamination) in addition to responsibility for sudden and accidental occurrences (e.g., fires or explosions).

Closure Cost Estimate [40 CFR 265.142]

Financial responsibility for the closure of storage facilities is integrated with the closure requirements of Subpart G. Section 265.142 of

Subpart H requires the preparation of an estimate, in current dollars, of the cost of closing the facility in accordance with the closure plan. This cost estimate must be prepared for the circumstances that would make closure of the facility the costliest. For storage facilities, this point would be when the amount of wastes in storage at the facility is at the facility design capacity. The closure cost estimate becomes part of the operating record.

The closure cost estimate must be adjusted annually for inflation. The existing closure cost estimate is multiplied by an inflation factor to get an adjusted cost estimate. The inflation factor is derived by dividing the latest annual implicit price deflator for gross national product by the implicit price deflator for the previous year. These figures are published by the U.S. Department of Commerce in its *Survey of Current Business*. The closure cost estimate must also be revised whenever a change in the closure plan increases the cost of closure.

The closure cost estimate provides the basis for the amount of financial assurance required for closure. Federal regulations provide five options for providing such assurance. State hazardous waste regulations may not allow certain of the federal options. The federal options are:

1. closure trust fund;
2. surety bond guaranteeing payment into a closure trust fund;
3. closure letter of credit;
4. closure insurance; and
5. financial test and corporate guarantee for closure.

Each of these mechanisms has very specific requirements as to when they may be used, the wording of the mechanism, cancellation provisions, etc. A detailed explanation of each is beyond the scope of this chapter. Waste management personnel should have the financial personnel at the manufacturing firm read the preamble and regulatory language regarding financial assurance for closure [46 FR 2802 and 47 FR 15032]. An examination of the state requirements and alternatives and their similarities to and differences from the federal mechanisms would then be in order. This information would form the basis of an intelligent decision regarding which of the available mechanisms best suits the firm's circumstances.

Liability Insurance

As mentioned earlier, financial responsibility includes liability insurance coverage for any bodily injury and property damage to third parties resulting from facility operations. Owner/operators of container and tank storage facilities need to demonstrate liability coverage for sudden accidental occurrences in minimum amounts of $1 million per occurrence, $2 million annual aggregate, exclusive of legal defense costs.

An amendment [47 FR 16554] to the financial assurance requirements allows for owners or operators to demonstrate the capability to self-insure. The regulations provide a financial test that, if met, will satisfy the regulatory requirements for liability coverage. Liability coverage may be provided through the use of a combination of the financial test and liability insurance.

It is interesting to note that many manufacturing facilities already possess liability insurance covering sudden accidental occurrences as part of their comprehensive general liability policies. Compliance with the regulatory standards merely requires assuring that the policy provides the specified amounts of coverage, verifying that the insurer is licensed to transact the business of insurance, and obtaining a certificate of insurance from the insurer. This certificate of liability insurance must be identical to that found at 40 CFR 264.151(j). The owner or operator is to submit a signed duplicate original to the federal and/or state regulatory authorities. The topic of insurance for hazardous waste management is covered in Chapter 23.

SUBPART I: USE AND MANAGEMENT OF CONTAINERS

Subpart I is discussed thoroughly in Chapter 10.

SUBPART J: TANKS

The regulatory requirements outlined in Subpart J are fairly straightforward and specific. The regulatory language is reiterated in Chapter 10.

CONSOLIDATED PERMIT REGULATIONS

Any discussion of the regulatory standards for interim status storage facilities is incomplete without mention of the consolidated permit regulations. The consolidated permit regulations consist of 40 CFR 122–124. These regulations are termed the "consolidated permit regulations" because they integrate certain federal permit programs and procedures and specify procedures for state assumption of regulatory and permitting authority for facilities regulated under the consolidated programs.

The regulatory programs covered by these regulations are:

1. the hazardous waste management program under RCRA;
2. the underground injection control (UIC) program under the Safe Drinking Water Act (SDWA);
3. the National Pollutant Discharge Elimination System (NPDES) program under the Clean Water Act (CWA);
4. the dredge or fill program under Section 404 of CWA; and
5. the prevention of significant deterioration (PSD) program under the Clean Air Act (CAA).

Basically, the consolidated permit regulations deal with the procedural aspects of permit issuance under the consolidated programs. Each regulatory program has regulations specifying the technical criteria for permit issuance in other regulations. For hazardous waste management facility permits, the technical criteria are found at 40 CFR 264.

Only a few sections of the consolidated permit regulations are of immediate interest to facilities under interim status. These sections will be covered first, and the remainder will be discussed briefly. Part 122 of 40 CFR, "Permit Requirements," specifies definitions to be used, and basic permit requirements for the RCRA, UIC and NPDES programs, including:

1. permit application requirements;
2. contents of the application;
3. mandatory conditions to the permit; and
4. revision, reissuance or termination of permits.

Of most interest to interim status facilities is Section 122.23, "Interim Status." Certain restrictions are placed on the operations of interim status facilities, in addition to the interim status standards found in Part 265.

During the interim status period, there are three restrictions imposed by Section 122.23. The facility shall not:

1. treat, store or dispose of a type of hazardous waste (by EPA hazardous waste number) that was not specified by the permit applicant in Part A of the permit application;

Table IX.   Compliance Program Documents[a]

Document	Regulatory Citation (40 CFR)	Potential Form	Maintained at Facility	Submitted to State and/or EPA Regional Office
1. Waste inventory and documentation surrounding hazardous/nonhazardous determination for each waste	262.11	Set of documents	X	
2. EPA Form 8700-12, Notification of Hazardous Waste Activity	262.12 and 265.11	Single document	(X)[b]	X
3. EPA Form 8700-12A, Acknowledgement of Notification of Hazardous Waste Activity with EPA Identification Number Assigned	265.11	Single document	(X)	
4. EPA Forms 3510-1 and 3510-3, Application for a Hazardous Waste Permit—Consolidated Permits Program	122.22	Single document	(X)	X
5. Waste analysis plan	265.13(b)	Single document	X	
6. Inspection schedule(s) • monitoring equipment • safety and emergency equipment • security devices • operating and structural equipment • container storage areas • tanks	265.15(b)	Single document	X	
7. Inspection Log or Summary	265.15(d)	Series of documents	X	
8. Job title for each position related to hazardous waste management and the name of the employee filling each job; job description for each position; description of introductory and continuing training; training records	265.16(d)	Set of documents	X	
9. Documentation of Testing and Maintenance of • facility communications or alarm systems • fire protection equipment • spill control equipment • decontamination equipment	265.16(e) 265.33	Series of documents	X	

Document	Regulatory Citation (40 CFR)	Potential Form	Maintained at Facility	Submitted to State and/or EPA Regional Office
10. Contingency plan	265.51	Set of documents		X
• description of planned responses to fires, explosions or unplanned releases of hazardous waste	265.52(a)			
• SPCC plan, if any	265.52(b)			
• arrangements/agreements with local authorities, including police department(s), fire department(s), hospitals, state and local emergency response teams, clean-up contractors and equipment suppliers	265.37 and 265.52(c)			
• emergency coordinator list	265.52(d)			
• list of emergency equipment, including location, physical description and capabilities of each item	265.52(c)			
• evacuation plan	265.52(f)			
11. Amendments to contingency plan	265.54	Series of documents	X	
12. Operating record	265.73	Set of documents	X	
• description and quantity of hazardous waste and method(s) and date(s) of TSD	265.73(b)(1)			
• location of each hazardous waste and quantity at each location	265.73(b)(2)			
• records and results of detailed chemical and physical analyses of each waste and any supplemental data	265.13(a) and 265.73(b)(3)			
• summary reports of any incidents requiring contingency plan implementation	265.73(b)(4)			
• closure cost estimates	265.142 and 265.73(b)(7)			
• documentation of any refusals by local authorities to enter into arrangements/agreements for contingency plan purposes	265.37(b)			
• records and results of inspections	265.15(d) and 265.73(b)(5)			

No.	Item	Regulation	Document form	(X)[b]	X[a]
13.	Annual report	262.41 and 265.75	Single document, annually	(X)	X[c]
14.	Closure plan	265.112	Single document	X	X[d]
15.	Certification of closure	265.115	Single document		X[e]
16.	Manifests and exception reports	262.40 and 265.71	Series of documents	X	X[f]
17.	Financial responsibility documentation		Set of documents	X	X
	• financial assurance for closure	265.143			
	• liability requirements	265.147			

[a] Adapted from "Plans, Recordkeeping, Variances, and Demonstrations for Hazardous Waste Treatment, Storage, and Disposal Facilities," SW-921, U.S. EPA, U.S. Government Printing Office (1981).

[b] For items marked (X), the regulations do not specify that they be maintained at the facility. However, it is advisable to maintain at the facility a copy of items submitted to the State and EPA Regional Office.

[c] Submitted by March 1 of each year.

[d] Submitted at least 180 days prior to commencement of closure activities.

[e] Submitted when closure is complete according to the approved closure plan.

[f] Submitted when generator has not received a signed copy of the manifest from the TSD within 45 days of the date of shipment.

2. employ processes not specified in Part A of the permit application; or
3. exceed the design capacities specified in Part A of the permit application.

Section 122.23 also allows for certain changes to the facility, its operations or its ownership under interim status. The requirements for permission to implement these changes are also specified in Section 122.23.

Other sections of interest in Part 122 are Section 122.24, "Contents of Part A," and Section 122.25, "Contents of Part B." Together, these sections specify the information requirements for a complete RCRA permit application.

Part 123, "State Program Requirements," of the consolidated permit regulations specifies the minimum requirements the various states must meet to obtain authorization to run a particular regulatory program. Authorization from EPA will enable the state to administer the regulatory program in lieu of, and with minimal interference from, EPA. Part 123 also contains the procedures for approval, revision, and withdrawal of authorization for state-run regulatory programs.

Finally, Part 124, "Procedures for Decisionmaking," specifies the permit review and issuance procedures to be used by EPA or an authorized state. Extensive public participation will be a part of every permit issued under these programs.

Parts 122–124 of the consolidated permits program have only limited impact on the operations of hazardous waste facilities under interim status. These regulations will be of much more interest and importance to the owners or operators of such facilities when Part B of their application is called in, or when a new hazardous waste facility is proposed.

SUMMARY

The regulatory requirements are fairly comprehensive for manufacturing firms as owner/operators of hazardous waste storage facilities. Compliance with these requirements will require the implementation of a formal waste management program. An important part of such a program will be the development of the documentation surrounding compliance. A list of required documents is given in Table IX. Section 3 deals with the development of a formal program, and the documentation required as part of such a program.

Chapter 12

GENERATORS WHO SHIP HAZARDOUS
WASTES OFFSITE

FEDERAL REQUIREMENTS

The requirements placed on generators who transport hazardous waste or offer hazardous waste for transportation offsite involve many pages of U.S. Department of Transportation (DOT) regulations. These are in addition to the requirements for accumulation or storage as discussed in Chapters 10 and 11. The U.S. Environmental Protection Agency (EPA) regulations for generators [40 CFR 262] and transporters [40 CFR 263] make frequent reference to the DOT hazardous materials transportation regulations [49 CFR 171–179]. In fact, the EPA standards applicable to generators who ship hazardous wastes offsite are largely indecipherable without a copy of the DOT regulations. However, the essence of the EPA/DOT standards for generators who ship offsite are simple. In essence, the generator has the responsibility for determining where the waste will undergo treatment, storage or disposal (TSD), and that the designated facility has the proper permits to accept the generator's particular type of waste. Further, the generator must see that the waste containers are in proper condition for transportation, that the transporter has a valid EPA identification number, and that the waste actually is received by the designated TSD facility. The many pages of regulatory standards merely apply this scheme to the endless variations possible due to the many types of wastes, types of containers and modes of transportation. Given these possible variations, a detailed explanation of the DOT hazardous material transportation regulations [49 CFR Parts 171–179] is beyond the scope of this book.

The key to understanding the DOT requirements for each particular type of waste is the hazardous materials table. Found at 49 CFR

172.101, the use of the hazardous materials table should be mastered by both generators ("shippers" in DOT jargon) and transporters ("carriers" in DOT jargon).

Materials and wastes designated by DOT as hazardous for shipping purposes are listed in the hazardous materials table along with the following information:

1. the proper shipping name (the word "waste" should be added as the first word of the proper shipping name when a listed material is shipped as a waste);
2. hazard classification;
3. UN/NA identification number;
4. required label(s);
5. references to where the specific packaging requirements are found in the DOT regulations; and
6. special requirements for water, rail or air transportation.

An understandable explanation of the EPA/DOT requirements for the transportation of hazardous wastes, as well as an explanation of how to use the hazardous materials table has been prepared for distribution by EPA. Entitled "EPA/DOT: Hazardous Waste Transportation Interface" (SW-935), this publication was available free at the time of this writing.

The requirements for generators who ship hazardous wastes offsite were mentioned briefly in Chapter 7. As indicated there, a whole series of requirements come into play once a generator decides to have a third party (the carrier) transport his hazardous waste to an offsite hazardous waste management facility. These requirements are:

1. The generator must determine the proper shipping name (including reportable quantity if applicable), hazard classification, and UN/NA number for manifest purposes [49 CFR 172.101, 172.203 and 173].
2. The generator must determine whether the proposed mode of transportation is prohibited by DOT regulations, or if additional shipping requirements must be met for the proposed transportation mode [49 CFR 172.101 and 174–177].
3. Compliance with DOT requirements for packaging [40 CFR 262.30 and 49 CFR 172, 178 and 179], labeling each package [40 CFR 262.31 and 49 CFR 172] and marking each package [40 CFR 262.32 and 49 CFR 172] must be assured.

4. The generator must verify that the proposed transporter and proposed TSD facility have valid EPA identification numbers [40 CFR 262.12(c)], as well as any other permits, licenses or approvals required by state and/or federal regulations.

5. The generator must prepare a manifest to accompany the movement of the hazardous wastes offsite. The manifest must contain all the information specified at 40 CFR 262.21, and must consist of a sufficient number of copies to provide the generator, each transporter and the designated TSD facility with one copy each for their records, and another copy to be returned to the generator by the TSD facility on receipt of the waste [40 CFR 262.22];

6. The generator must offer the transporter the appropriate placards or determine that the vehicle is appropriately placarded [49 CFR 172, Subpart F and 40 CFR 262.33].

7. The generator must sign the manifest, certifying that the waste shipment meets all EPA and DOT pretransportation requirements [40 CFR 262.21(b)].

8. The generator must obtain the signature of the transporter and the date of acceptance on the manifest. The generator is to retain one copy and give the remaining copies of the manifest to the transporter [40 CFR 262.32].

9. The generator must keep a copy of each manifest signed for three years or until a manifest copy signed by the designated TSD facility is received. This latter copy must then be held as a record for at least three years from the date the waste was accepted by the initial transporter.

10. The generator must monitor the manifest tracking system. Administrative procedures must be in place whereby the failure to receive, within 35 days, a copy of the manifest with the signature of the owner or operator of the TSD facility will trigger an investigation into the status of the hazardous waste shipment. The generator is then to contact the transporter and the designated TSD facility to determine the status or location of the hazardous waste and the manifest. If a copy of the manifest with the handwritten signature of the owner or operator of the designated TSD facility is not received within 45 days from the initial date of shipment, then the generator must file with EPA what is known as an exception report, including a copy of the manifest covering the shipment in question and an explanation of efforts taken to locate the hazardous waste.

11. The generator must submit annual reports covering the types and amounts of hazardous wastes shipped offsite during the previous calendar year. The annual report names the transporters and TSD facilities used. For each facility used, the quantity and the type (by EPA waste description and DOT hazard class) of wastes received must be given.

12. The generator must keep records of manifests, annual reports, exception reports, test results, waste analyses and determinations performed under 262.11. Each of these records must be kept for a minimum of three years (longer if requested). The starting date for the three year period varies with the type of document [262.40].

STATE REQUIREMENTS

A discussion of regulatory standards for generators who ship wastes offsite is incomplete without mention of potential state requirements. Many states have waste transportation requirements or waste hauler licensing or permit programs. Some of these requirements predate the Resource Conservation and Recovery Act (RCRA) hazardous waste regulations by several years. As a result, there may be a different regulatory focus than that of RCRA, such as on liquid industrial wastes, industrial wastes or hazardous wastes using a pre-RCRA definition. Contact the state solid/hazardous waste management agencies for the state(s) through which the firm's hazardous waste will be traveling for information on the existence of any such requirements.

State variations from the federal hazardous waste management system can include the requirement to send copies of the manifest to the state regulatory agency. This requirement is occasionally combined with the required use of a state-specified format or form. A five- or six-part manifest (or copies) may be required if a manifest copy must be submitted to the state agency. States can require the generator and/or the TSD facility to submit a copy.

Manifest requirements become even more confused when hazardous waste is shipped to a TSD facility in another state. In this situation, it is possible that two (or more) manifests must accompany the shipment, depending on the official form requirements of the various states the shipment passes through. In addition, manifest copies may need to be sent to state agencies in the state in which the waste was generated and the state in which the waste was treated/disposed.

UNIFORM NATIONAL MANIFEST

The compliance problems caused by the sometimes inconsistent state requirements led to the proposal of a uniform national manifest [47 FR 9336]. The uniform national manifest form would supersede any existing state manifest forms, and would render obsolete any existing commercial manifest forms. At the time of this writing, the uniform manifest was still a proposal. However, the regulatory agenda of the EPA [47 FR 15702] indicates that the joint EPA/DOT rulemaking should be in final rule form around December 1982. When finalized, the federal uniform national manifest form would be the only permissible manifest form.

SUMMARY

The basic elements of the regulatory scheme generators must follow in preparing hazardous wastes for shipment offsite are simple. However, the regulations that apply this scheme to the many types of wastes, types of containers and modes of transportation are lengthy and complex. Needless to say, the services of a transporter (carrier) knowledgeable in the DOT hazardous materials transportation regulations can be invaluable. The use of a carrier specializing in hazardous waste hauling may be beneficial to the firm's compliance efforts. Of course, the generator is ultimately responsible for many of the transportation requirements, and should at least be generally familiar with the transportation regulations and able to use the hazardous materials table.

Chapter 13

GENERATORS WHO TREAT HAZARDOUS WASTES BY AN EXEMPTED METHOD

As might be expected, generators who treat hazardous wastes by an exempted method have few regulatory standards to abide by. The regulatory definition of treatment, found at 40 CFR 260.10, is as follows:

> "Treatment" means any method, technique, or process, including neutralization, designed to change the physical, chemical, or biological character or composition of any hazardous waste so as to neutralize such waste, or so as to recover energy or material resources from the waste, or so as to render such waste non-hazardous, or less hazardous; safer to transport, store, or dispose of; or amenable for recovery, amenable for storage, or reduced in volume.

The inclusive nature of this definition is important because it is combined with requirements that persons owning or operating a hazardous waste treatment facility apply for a Resource Conservation and Recovery Act (RCRA) permit and comply with interim status standards. Thus, the broad nature of the definition and the associated requirements make any exemptions all the more important.

EXEMPTIONS UNDER 40 CFR 265.1(c)

Chapter 5 listed the treatment facilities and methods that are exempted from regulation. Neither the permit requirements nor the interim status standards apply to owners or operators of nonregulated treatment facilities. However, such facilities can still be generators of hazardous wastes. The exemptions of most interest to manufacturing facilities are those granted to:

1. facilities permitted by a state to manage municipal or industrial solid waste, if the only hazardous wastes the facility treats, stores or disposes of are produced by small-quantity generators [40 CFR 265.1(c)(5) and 122.21(d)(2)];
2. facilities that treat or store characteristic hazardous wastes (except sludges) before use, reuse, recycling or reclamation [40 CFR 265.1(c)(6)];
3. totally enclosed treatment facilities [40 CFR 265.1(c)(9) and 122.21(d)(2)];
4. elementary neutralization units or wastewater treatment units [40 CFR 265.1(c)(10) and 122.21(d)(2)];
5. publicly owned treatment works (POTW), also known as municipal sewage treatment plants, that treat, store or dispose of hazardous waste [40 CFR 265.1(c)(3)];
6. activities carried out to immediately contain or treat a spill of hazardous waste [40 CFR 265.1(c)(11) and 122.21(c)(3)]; and
7. addition of absorbent material to waste at the time waste is first placed into containers [40 CFR 265.1(c)(13) and 122.21(c)(2)].

Exemption 1 [40 CFR 265.1(c)(5)]

Facilities permitted by a state to manage municipal or industrial solid wastes have onsite and offsite implications for the small-quantity generator. The onsite implications involve the potential use of existing onsite disposal or treatment facilities for managing the hazardous wastes of the small-quantity generator owner/operator. These hazardous wastes would be in addition to the wastes already being managed at the onsite facility. Of course, the facility should already have a state permit or should obtain one before managing the small quantities of hazardous waste generated by the owner/operator. One caveat is necessary—obtain written permission and/or the relevant permit amendments from the state regulatory agency before onsite treatment or disposal under this exclusion. Further, onsite disposal of hazardous wastes is generally not a very good idea, considering the potential costs and liabilities associated with disposal.

The offsite implications of the first category apply to the treatment or disposal of hazardous wastes from a small-quantity generator at sanitary landfills, or other facilities permitted by a state to manage municipal or industrial solid wastes. This topic is discussed in Chapter 8.

Exemption 2 [40 CFR 265.1(c)(6)]

Facilities that treat or store characteristic hazardous wastes before recycling are fairly straightforward. Like the first category, there are onsite and offsite implications. The topic is thoroughly discussed in Chapter 9.

Exemption 3 [40 CFR 265.1(c)(9)]

The meaning of the definition of a "totally enclosed treatment facility" remains a mystery to this day. The regulatory definition found at 40 CFR 260.10 is:

> a facility for the treatment of hazardous waste which is directly connected to an industrial production process and which is constructed and operated in a manner which prevents the release of any hazardous waste or any constituent thereof into the environment during treatment. An example is a pipe in which acid is neutralized.

Given this example, it is doubtful that many treatment facilities could qualify for this exemption. If it is believed that a particular treatment process or operation qualifies for the exemption, it would be wise to get a letter to that effect from the U.S. Environmental Protection Agency (EPA) and the state regulatory agency. The state hazardous waste and water pollution control organizations may need to be involved if the facility involves a wastewater discharge.

Exemption 4 [40 CFR 265.1(c)(10)]

The elementary neutralization unit/wastewater treatment unit exemption was published in the *Federal Register* [45 FR 76074]. This exempted, in one fell swoop, a large percentage of industrial National Pollutant Discharge Elimination System (NPDES) operations and industrial pretreatment operations. This amendment suspended the applicability of 40 CFR 122, 264 and 265 to owners and operators of

> (1) wastewater treatment tanks that receive, store, and treat wastewaters that are hazardous waste or that generate, store or treat a wastewater treatment sludge which is a hazardous waste where such wastewaters are subject to regulation under Sections 402 or 307(b) of the Clean Water Act (33 U.S.C. 1251 et seq.) and
> (2) neutralization tanks, transport vehicles, vessels, or containers which neutralize wastes which are hazardous only because they exhibit the corrosivity characteristic under 40 CFR 261.22 or are

listed as hazardous wastes in Subpart D of 40 CFR Part 261 only
for that reason [45 FR 76074].

The crucial element of this exemption is the regulatory definition of
"tank," which is referenced in the regulatory definitions of "elementary
neutralization unit" and "wastewater treatment unit." The definition
of tank is found at 40 CFR 260.10, and reads as follows: "a stationary
device, designed to contain an accumulation of hazardous waste,
which is constructed primarily of non-earthen materials (e.g., wood,
concrete, steel, plastic) which provide structural support."

The definition is meant to distinguish tanks from surface impoundments. A concrete-lined pit would be a surface impoundment, not a
tank. The general rule of thumb is whether the unit would be self-
supporting, were it removed from the ground. Nonearthen materials
must provide the structural support.

The importance of the wastewater treatment unit/elementary neutralization unit exemption is self-evident. Such facilities do not require
a RCRA permit, under the assumption that an NPDES permit or industrial pretreatment permit is sufficient. Further, the standards for
owner/operators of treatment facilities [40 CFR 264 and 265] do not
apply to the units themselves. This exemption, by implication, allows
the manufacturing facility to order its waste management operations
so as to be a generator (only), and thus subject only to the 40 CFR
262 and 263 standards. The regulatory standards for generators are discussed in Chapter 7.

Also contained in the November 17, 1980, *Federal Register* was a
proposed rule [45 FR 76076] regarding special standards for owner/
operators of elementary neutralization units and wastewater treatment
units. Additionally, a permit-by-rule would be available for such owners or operators, provided they complied with the special standards.
Because this was a proposal, and not a final or interim final amendment
or rule, it is not in effect. The regulatory agenda of the EPA [47 FR
15702] indicated that the EPA intends to impose some form of minimal
controls and requirements on elementary neutralization units and
wastewater treatment units.

Exemption 5 [40 CFR 265.1(c)(3)]

The fifth category of interest is the exemption given to POTW, also
known as sewage treatment plants. This exemption is of interest only
to manufacturing firms that discharge industrial wastes to a sewer system connected to a POTW.

In addition to the exclusion given the POTW [265.1(c)(3)], the regulations exclude from the definition of solid waste "any mixture of domestic sewage and other wastes that passes through a sewer system to a publicly-owned treatment works for treatment" [261.4(a)(1)(ii)]. Thus, if the manufacturing facility can obtain permission from the municipal sewage treatment authority, the specified hazardous wastes may be discharged legally to municipal sewers. The two regulatory provisions combine to exempt both the generator and POTW from the hazardous waste management system for those wastes so managed.

It must be emphasized that the manufacturing facility should obtain written permission for any hazardous wastes (and other industrial wastes) discharged to the sewer system. Many municipalities will require some degree of treatment (termed "pretreatment") prior to discharge to the sewer. In addition, the pretreatment equipment may need a permit from the municipality or the state water pollution control agency. If the pretreatment operation does not qualify for the elementary neutralization unit/wastewater treatment unit exclusion discussed above, then it will also require a hazardous waste treatment permit.

Exemption 6 [40 CFR 265.1(c)(11)]

The sixth is that regarding action taken immediately to contain or treat a hazardous waste spill. However, the preparedness and prevention regulations [40 CFR 265, Subpart C] and the contingency plan and emergency procedures requirements [40 CFR 265, Subpart D] must be complied with during all aspects of spill response. After the immediate response is over, the regulations apply fully to the management of any spill residue or debris which is a hazardous waste.

Exemption 7 [40 CFR 265.1(c)(13)]

The last treatment exclusion of interest to manufacturing facilities is that surrounding the treatment method generically known as "solidification." Solidification is a general term for the act of adding absorbent material to liquid wastes and wastes of a semisolid consistency. The purpose of solidification is to eliminate what are known as "free liquids" and "free-standing liquids" by absorbing them. By so doing, liquid and semisolid wastes can be disposed of legally at a hazardous waste landfill. The hazardous waste regulations for landfills prohibit the disposal of free liquids or containers holding free liquids unless such liquids are removed or solidified [40 CFR 265.314(b)].

The terms "free liquids" and "free-standing liquids" refer to liquids that readily separate from the solid portion of a waste. Test protocols are found at 45 FR 33214 and 47 FR 8313. Examples of commonly used absorbents include expanded clay, cement kiln dust, fly ash, fuller's earth, vermiculite and commercial absorbents using synthetic media. It is becoming common practice for generators to add absorbents to drums containing semisolids or sludges. This prevents any free liquids from separating due to vibration during transportation. Disposal facilities are required to check each shipment for free liquids. A shipment containing drums with free-standing liquids may be rejected by the landfill and returned to the generator. Often, such shipments are assessed an off-specification surcharge, added to the disposal cost. This is to cover the removal or solidification of any free liquid by the landfill operator.

To conclude this subject it is necessary to reiterate the exemption, namely, that the addition of absorbent material to hazardous waste in containers or the addition of waste to absorbent material in containers is exempt from the regulations. However, this solidification must take place at the time the waste is first placed in the container.

PICKLE LIQUOR [46 FR 44972]

A final note is necessary to complete the topic of exempted treatment methods. The EPA has excluded from the regulations spent pickle liquor which is reused in wastewater treatment at a facility holding a NPDES permit, or which is being accumulated, stored or treated before such reuse [46 FR 44972]. Thus, the treatment of pickle liquor by its use for phosphorus removal or as a coagulation aid in an NPDES-permitted facility is exempt under the beneficial use, reuse, recycling and reclamation provisions [261.6(a)(3)].

SUMMARY

The use of exempted treatment methods is a legal method of relieving some of the regulatory burdens associated with the present regulatory scheme. The exemptions are designed to afford the required degree of environmental protection without the necessity of formal standards and permit requirements. In the case of wastewater treatment, there are still regulatory standards under the Clean Water Act to abide by. It is assumed that generators will still use good judgment in treating their hazardous wastes under one of the exemptions.

SECTION 3

DEVELOPING THE CORPORATE
COMPLIANCE PROGRAM

Many manufacturing firms have yet to implement a compliance program to meet the hazardous waste management requirements. There are many reasons for this situation, not the least of which are the complexity of the regulations and the lack of guidance.

The chapters in Section 2 specified the requirements applicable to the various regulatory categories. Guidance and interpretation of the regulations were provided when necessary. Section 3 builds on the information given previously, enabling waste managers to integrate the various requirements into a comprehensive compliance program.

Chapter 14

LEAST-COST COMPLIANCE WITH HAZARDOUS WASTE MANAGEMENT REGULATIONS

One of the very welcome results of the implementation of the hazardous waste regulations has been the unleashing of the ingenuity and initiative of waste management personnel at manufacturing firms. Management of industrial wastes has been elevated to a legitimate concern, and no longer is viewed merely as an annoyance. Waste management personnel have responded to this new focus of corporate management, regulatory officials and the public by finding innovative means of compliance with the letter and spirit of the regulations, at reasonable cost to their employers.

It appears that the imposition of the strict set of ground rules governing hazardous waste management (HWM) has finally allowed waste management personnel to justify process changes and waste management methods that reduce the generation of wastes designated "hazardous" and/or requiring land disposal. Strategies that achieve such results are central to the goal of least-cost compliance.

The mechanism by which such efforts are allowed and encouraged is that of the market system. Higher prices for treatment and disposal as a result of the Resource Conservation and Recovery Act (RCRA) regulations now justify in-plant modifications and methods that previously were uneconomical. It is not the author's intention to discuss the concepts of demand, supply, prices or other academic niceties. The purpose of this chapter is to examine process changes and waste management methods that have been adopted by certain manufacturing firms in the pursuit of the desirable goal of least-cost compliance. Chapter 15 will attempt to integrate these methods into a residuals management strategy.

Before outlining methods and strategies, it is useful to list the organizational factors that are necessary for individuals within the industrial environment to investigate, develop and apply innovative approaches in meeting the requirements of the regulations. These factors are:

1. corporate policy requiring strict compliance with the letter and spirit of pollution control laws and regulations;
2. designation of an individual responsible for compliance with pollution control requirements, and delegation of the necessary authority, technical support and financial resources to meet that goal (a waste management committee could be established to assist this individual);
3. flexibility at the plant level to experiment with different inputs, process changes, or operating procedures; and
4. availability of discretionary capital for changes that are cost-effective, taking into consideration both short- and long-term costs and benefits.

Strategies and methods that have begun appearing in organizations pursuing least-cost compliance are not novel, but have been little used because of the ease and low cost of land disposal. At present and for the foreseeable future, land disposal will be neither cheap nor easy, and in fact is now realized to be difficult, uncertain and posing certain long-term risks. The discussion and industrial application of strategies and methods to reduce waste generation and reliance on land disposal suggest that the concept of least-cost compliance is no longer viewed as an ivory-tower suggestion.

The following steps have been used by many waste-generating industries with successful least-cost compliance programs.

EXAMINATION OF WASTE STREAMS

This effort is to categorize all the different waste streams requiring management by type, composition and quantity. It appears as if two categories cover most streams: process wastes and pollution control residuals. However, a waste inventory can reveal surprising amounts of off-specification input materials, defective outputs, inadvertent contamination of inputs, process chemicals and outputs, and obsolete (expired) chemical products. The conduct of a waste inventory was discussed in Chapter 3.

Particular attention should be given to potential problem areas. These include excessive waste amounts per unit of production, excessive process upsets or bad batches, or frequent receipt of off-specification inputs. Some effort should be expended to determine the effect of process variables on the waste streams created, and the relationship of waste stream composition to the input chemicals and process methods used. The amount of water used by different processes and the possibilities for reuse could also be examined at this time.

WASTE STREAM ANALYSIS

Even though the RCRA regulations do not require a generator to test his waste streams to determine if they are hazardous [40 CFR 262.11], it is required that the generator determine if a waste is a hazardous waste. Chemical analysis using proper and uniform sampling procedures, and the specified analytical and testing methods and procedures can most accurately determine the nature of the waste and can yield valuable information about the industrial process and the condition of the equipment. Additionally, such information is necessary to determine the feasibility of reuse, recycling, reclamation, materials recovery or waste transfer, or the proper methods of treatment or disposal.

MATERIAL SUBSTITUTIONS

The information gathered by the waste stream examination and analysis can suggest or justify the substitution of certain input or process materials or chemicals so that the process wastes and pollution control residuals would no longer be of a hazardous nature.

It may then be possible to discharge certain waste streams to the municipal sewer system (with municipal approval, of course), saving money on the transportation and disposal of those liquid industrial wastes previously needing treatment or disposal at offsite facilities. Examples of this include substitution of alkaline cleaning solutions for organic solvents, use of water-based paints instead of oil-based paints and replacing emulsified oil coolants with synthetic coolants. Another possible outcome would be that the waste stream could be managed by state-licensed land disposal facilities, rather than RCRA-permitted facilities or facilities under interim status. This outcome has been enjoyed by those firms in the industrial painting field that have switched from paints with high heavy metal content to paints with much lower levels.

PROCESS DESIGN CHANGES

Modifications of production systems with the goal of minimizing hazardous residuals often come to mind, or are indicated by the information gathered by examination and analysis of waste streams. Many individuals are looking at industrial processes as a system, with inputs and outputs. Outputs include both the intended product, and the solid, liquid and gaseous residuals needing management. There is a movement away from strictly "end-of-pipe" approaches, where treatment and disposal methods are designed and operated for any quantity of waste produced. Process changes can be introduced to reduce the capacity and cost of necessary pollution control equipment and the cost of disposal. Such in-plant corrections and modifications can pay for themselves. The objective is to reduce waste stream quantities or lower the concentration levels to the point where further reduction is more expensive than treatment or disposal of the wastes that remain. This brings us back to economics. Effluent reduction, neutralization and pretreatment should be used where cost-effective. Short- and long-term costs and benefits should be factored into the decision to modify the process or acquire the necessary equipment.

IN-HOUSE REUSE

The goal of this strategy is to maximize the useful lifetime of process chemicals. This is accomplished by methods that will keep contaminant levels and chemical concentrations within specifications. Methods used to delay system flushing and replacement include prevention of contamination, filtration, water removal, oil skimming, solids removal, bacterial control and chemical replenishment to maintain desirable concentration levels.

In-house reuse includes using spent chemicals for a different purpose. An example of this is the use of waste petroleum products as supplemental boiler fuels.

SEGREGATION OF WASTE STREAMS

Segregation of the distinct types of waste streams identified and analyzed makes overall management of these wastes easier. Proper segregation prevents normally nonhazardous wastes from becoming hazardous by virtue of being mixed with a listed hazardous waste [40 CFR 261.3]. Such actions allow for management of concentrated waste streams rather than large volumes of mixed and diluted wastes. Concentrated waste streams make recycling or waste transfer easier. Segregation requires and allows the proper packaging, labeling and marking necessitated by 40 CFR 262.30-32. Segregation also makes manifesting [40 CFR 262.21] and transportation easier and lessens the possibility of mistakes. Segregation also meets the requirements for incompatible wastes [40 CFR 265.177] and makes inspections easier [40 CFR 265.174].

WASTE TRANSFER

Waste transfer is the movement of wastes and manufacturing by-products from firms that find no use or value in them to firms that can use such materials as substitutes for materials and chemicals otherwise purchased in a virgin state. Specifications for chemical quality, purity and concentration vary widely among different users; thus, transfer is possible to users that have lower specifications or that can use a lower-quality chemical. Examples of transferable wastes include spent acids, solvents and paint strippers. Spent pickling liquors from steel finishing operations are used in some sewage treatment plants as flocculant aids and for phosphorus removal.

In general, transfers can take place between large companies with continuous processes to smaller companies using batch processes; from basic chemical manufacturers to chemical formulators and users; from industries with high purity requirements to those with lower purity requirements.

Several organizations have evolved to promote the concept of waste transfer. Generally called "waste exchanges," they publish anonymous or "blind" listings of wastes or by-products available and wastes or by-products desired. Waste exchanges operate in many states. Appendix 4 lists waste exchanges.

RECYCLING/MATERIAL AND ENERGY RECOVERY

Recycling is similar in concept to waste transfer, except that some processing (e.g., filtration, distillation and rerefining) is necessary before the material can be used again. Wastes generally recognized as having components of potential value include:

1. sludges having high concentrations of recoverable metals,
2. precious metals,
3. solvents,
4. acids and alkalis,
5. oils,
6. catalysts, and
7. combustible liquids (for fuel).

In the commercial recycling market, wastes can be reprocessed for reuse by the original generator, or are sold to a third party by the recycling firm. Additionally, wastes can be processed to meet the purity specifications of the virgin chemical, or to be useful only in another application. For example, a spent solvent can be reclaimed to be reused in the process from which it was taken, or it can be reclaimed sufficiently to serve only as a cleanup solvent or supplemental boiler fuel.

TREATMENT

Even with process modifications and material substitutions, there may still be waste streams requiring some type of onsite treatment before discharge to a municipal sewer or a waterway. Additionally, some treatment (neutralization, detoxication) is necessary before certain waste streams can be managed by land disposal. Dewatering of waste streams has assumed additional importance now that special requirements and restrictions on the disposal of liquid wastes (and wastes containing free liquids) in hazardous waste landfills are in effect [40 CFR 265.314]. Dewatering will also reduce quantities needing transportation and disposal.

It is important to understand federal, state and local pollution control regulations before purchasing any particular type of pollution control equipment. Air and water pollution control equipment should be chosen knowing the types and amounts of pollution control residuals that will result from their operation. Ideally, the cost of disposal of such residuals should be factored into the decision to purchase. Finally, innovative technologies for waste treatment and control should be investigated.

RETURNABLE BARRELS

The use of returnable barrels for raw material or process chemicals may seem a minor consideration, but their use can prevent unnecessary disposal costs. Deposits range $20–$200. The services of a barrel re-claimer are also a possibility. EPA published [45 FR 78529] a clarifi-cation of its regulation of hazardous wastes in containers. Although the hazardous waste residue in "empty" containers is not subject to the reg-ulations [40 CFR 261.7(a)], other standards preventing the disposal of uncrushed barrels in landfills will cause the cost of empty barrel dis-posal to rise [40 CFR 265.315].

SUMMARY

It is hoped that this information may be of value to generators that have not begun pursuit of the goal of least-cost compliance. The dili-gent application of individual intelligence, creativity and ingenuity toward this goal may make the imposition of strict controls on hazard-ous waste management more palatable to both the employees involved and their employers. RCRA is a law conceived with good intentions, but it will require trained professionals with an innovative approach to enable these good intentions to be transformed into environmentally sound actions.

Chapter 15

IMPLEMENTING A RESIDUALS MANAGEMENT STRATEGY FOR ENVIRONMENTAL COMPLIANCE

The nature and complexity of current environmental laws and regulations present a challenge to the persons responsible for compliance. The sheer bulk of the regulations regarding air and water effluents and solid/hazardous waste management pose almost insurmountable reading for such people. Further, compliance efforts with respect to one environmental medium (air, water or land) may adversely affect compliance efforts in another.

There are a number of different methods available for managing the solid, liquid and gaseous residuals (often called "wastes") associated with a manufacturing operation. There are also many intricacies and interactions involved in complying with the separate sets of regulations protecting the air, water and land. The high costs of compliance (or noncompliance) seem to indicate the advantages of a structured approach, integrating efforts to comply with the separate sets of regulations. Using the "black box" analogy described in Chapter 3, such an approach could be termed a "residuals management" strategy.

This chapter is an attempt to describe a residuals management strategy with respect to the solid and liquids residuals (wastes) of manufacturing operations. This chapter builds on the concept of least-cost compliance introduced in Chapter 14, and integrates the activities described there into the framework offered by the waste management hierarchy.

STRUCTURED APPROACH

As with any complex problem, the first step in a structured approach for environmental compliance is to outline the overall goals. Possible goals for a residuals management strategy are:

147

1. to minimize total environmental compliance costs (short- and long-term);
2. to avoid environmental damage from facility operations;
3. to minimize corporate short- and long-term liability from residuals (waste) management; and
4. to fulfill corporate responsibilities and maintain a good corporate image.

A waste management hierarchy applicable to the situation is as follows (in order of desirability):

-   prevent the generation of waste (hazardous and nonhazardous);
-   minimize the proportion of unavoidable waste that is hazardous;
-   separate and concentrate waste streams to make further management activities easier;
-   reuse internally or use offsite through waste transfer;
-   recycle or reclaim energy and material values from the waste;
-   maintain unavoidable and nonreclaimable wastes in a form amenable to neutralization, detoxication, precipitation, incineration or destruction, and perform such operations to render the treatment residue and effluent less hazardous or nonhazardous; and
-   manage remaining hazardous wastes by secure land disposal, and manage remaining nonhazardous wastes by sanitary landfill.

While deciding how the hierarchy applies to facility operations, two important points must be remembered. First, it must be realized that just because a waste does not fall within the U.S. Environmental Protection Agency (EPA) definition of hazardous waste, it should not be inferred that the waste poses no threat to the environment. Nonhazardous status for waste streams does not relieve the generator of responsibility for their proper management. The second consideration of importance is that certain activities under the waste management hierarchy are regulated activities, and require a permit before construction or operation of any facilities. This second consideration refers specifically to the treatment of hazardous waste. The definition of treatment. found at 40 CFR 260.10, is as follows:

> Any method, technique, or process, including neutralization, designed to change the physical, chemical, or biological character or composition of any hazardous waste so as to neutralize such waste, or so as to recover energy or material resources from the waste, or so as to render such waste non-hazardous or less haz-

ardous; safer to transport, store, or dispose of; or amenable for recovery, amenable for storage, or reduced in volume.

This broad definition, combined with the Resource Conservation and Recovery Act (RCRA) Section 3005 requirements that any person owning or operating a hazardous waste treatment, storage or disposal (TSD) facility obtain a RCRA permit, presents certain administrative requirements before any actual implementation of treatment activities. These administrative activities include, at a minimum, completing EPA forms 8700-12, "Notification of Hazardous Waste Activity," and 3510-1 and 3510-3, "Application for a Hazardous Waste Permit—Consolidated Permits Program." Both documents are to be submitted to the EPA regional office with jurisdiction for the state in which the facility is located. Similar application should be made to the state regulatory authority. Construction or operation may not be allowed for certain facilities or activities until final disposition is made on the permit application. State hazardous waste management permit requirements often parallel the federal program, and the permit process can often proceed simultaneously at both levels.

Because of these requirements, it is necessary to be able to track the flow of residuals (wastes) through the plant. Waste management personnel must be able to establish exactly where a residual becomes a hazardous waste and the point at which any treatment residue and effluent become nonhazardous. The ability to segregate and manage each waste stream at the point of origin is also important. Such a tracking system implies a "chain of custody" concept, in which specific individuals are responsible for residuals (waste) management within specific portions of plant operations.

What follow are specific suggestions, relevant questions and activities that could be used in implementing the waste management hierarchy. Their nature and applicability under different steps in the hierarchy preclude a simple listing under each level of the hierarchy.

PROCESS MODIFICATIONS/INPUT SUBSTITUTIONS

Could different (nonhazardous) process chemicals and/or different production processes (yielding nonhazardous residuals) result in the same or equivalent quality of product outputs?

Do purity and concentration requirements for process chemicals bear some relation to process needs? For example, could opportunities for extended life and reuse of process baths be created through more realistic specifications, with no decrease in finished product quality? Do specifications call for virgin products only?

Could spent solutions be reclaimed to sufficient purity and concentrations for reuse in the process? Could spent solutions be reclaimed to sufficient purity for reuse by others?

An examination of the market requirements for the finished product may be in order. For example, is the surface finish for appearance or durability? Are less-polluting finish processes available which would meet market demands? Would customers be willing to accept lower quality of appearance as a tradeoff for a lower price?

Do process steps bear a realistic relationship to need? How clean is clean enough? How many rinses/how much rinse water is sufficient?

Do production and process variables have any relationship to the amount of wastes generated per unit of output? Are "economies" achieved at high production levels, or during continuous (24 hr/day) operation, or is there a linear relation between production and waste generation?

Specific examples of some of the activities possible under this category include:

1. substitution of alkaline cleaning solutions for chlorinated organic solvents;
2. powder paint application replacing the use of spray application in a water-wall paint booth;
3. water-based paints in lieu of solvent-based paints;
4. use of aluminum in place of chrome-plated steel;
5. use of synthetic coolants in place of emulsified oil coolants; and
6. use of spray rinses rather than rinse baths.

BEST MANAGEMENT PRACTICES

Prevention of Contamination of Process Chemicals by Proper Process Design and Plant Layout

These practices may include the use of rinses, or covered or closed storage tanks and process baths. Dragout can be minimized by allowing proper drainage of dipped parts above process baths, and production lines can be designed to avoid activities above open baths.

Prevention of Leakage and Spills

These practices include maintenance, inspection, repair, and replacement activities to avoid leaky baths or ruptured storage tanks. Spills can be minimized by adequate freeboard in open tanks, and proper startup, shutdown, maintenance, chemical addition and material transfer procedures.

Extension of Useful Life of Process Chemicals

Activities under this heading include some previously discussed. Prevention of contamination is one of the best ways to extend the life of a chemical bath. Similarly, dilution of process baths by rinse water can be minimized by spray rinsing or by allowing adequate time for drainage. Depletion of the necessary chemicals can be corrected by periodic additions. Maintenance of process baths at the necessary levels of purity and concentration determines just how long solution lifetimes can be extended. A management system where the process baths are tested periodically for specific parameters, with subsequent filtration/ dewatering/solids removal/oil skimming/bacterial control/precipitation/reclamation and replenishment would prevent any unnecessary wastage and extend solution lifetimes to the greatest extent. Portable equipment could be improvised for these purposes.

Segregation and Concentration of Wastes

The ability to trace the flow of residuals through the plant allows the management of concentrated waste streams by segregation. Proper segregation prevents normally nonhazardous wastes from becoming hazardous by virtue of being mixed with a listed hazardous waste. Concentrated waste streams make recycling or waste transfer easier. Segregation also allows for easier compliance with requirements for wastes to be treated or disposed offsite. The ability to trace residual flows (sometimes called "waste streams"), and their subsequent segregation also allows for easier compliance with storage requirements. Storage without a permit is allowed for up to 90 days. The clock is started the day the hazardous waste is first accumulated in a storage container. This date is to be marked on the container, along with certain other information. Storage is a necessary waste management practice, performed to accumulate sufficient quantities of concentrated wastes for batch treatment, or for transportation to offsite facilities for further management.

Waste Transfer

Although this is not a technique to prevent or minimize the generation of hazardous wastes, it does reduce the amounts of waste requiring land disposal. Waste transfer is the physical movement of wastes and manufacturing by-products from firms that find no use or value in them to firms that can use such materials as substitutes for materials and chemicals otherwise purchased in a virgin state. Specifications for chemical quality, purity and concentration vary widely among different users; thus, transfer is possible to users with lower specifications.

Recycling/Material and Energy Recovery

Recycling and reuse have been discussed above as they apply to on-site recovery with reuse in the same application. An entire industry has developed around the concept of processing industrial wastes so that they may be reused again in the same or a different application. These commercial facilities extract the components of value from the wastes, and either return the recovered materials to the generator, or sell them to another user. Often the component of value is the energy content of the waste stream. Processed petroleum-based waste streams are often used as supplemental fuels for industrial boilers.

SUMMARY

The complexity of the ever-growing body of environmental regulations and the high costs of compliance (or noncompliance) seem to indicate the advantages of a residuals management approach to environmental compliance. Such an approach for solid and liquid wastes would have least-cost compliance as a goal, and would use the waste management hierarchy in determining actions toward this goal.

This approach is a more involved undertaking than merely meeting each requirement separately, without perceiving the total effect of the environmental regulations on the manufacturing process or the effect of changes in the manufacturing process on compliance with the regulations. Interactions include the effect of compliance methods for one set of environmental requirements on the applicability of and compliance with other environmental regulations.

An integrated residuals management approach toward compliance points to the use of the team concept. A residuals or waste management committee could be established, involving the talents of representatives from various company activities. As a first cut, personnel from purchasing, plant engineering, production, pollution control/industrial hygiene and finance could be included.

This committee would be responsible for developing a residuals management strategy capable of meeting all environmental requirements at least-cost to the company. The committee should examine alternatives and present recommendations to management. It is hoped that Chapters 14 and 15 will provide a starting point for discussion.

Chapter 16

EFFECTIVE USE OF ENVIRONMENTAL AUDITS IN THE PLANT

Timothy M. Kelley

> Roll Coater Inc.
> Division of Arvin Industries
> Greenfield, Indiana

Gary F. Lindgren

> Engineering Section
> Division of Land Pollution Control
> Indiana State Board of Health
> Indianapolis, Indiana

An environmental audit is one of the most important methods available to waste management personnel in evaluating the degree of compliance of the firm. Although audits can include air pollution, water pollution, and occupational health and safety compliance reviews, this chapter will focus on solid and hazardous waste management practices. The information gathered through the audit will provide the basis for a corporate compliance program.

An environmental audit can serve several purposes, including:

1. identification of and planning for future pollution control investments, which can include those that will prevent, reclaim or reduce wastes as discussed in Chapters 14 and 15;
2. compliance with Security and Exchange Commission requirement 10-K, which involves disclosure of environmental compliance problems and anticipated future compliance expenditures;

3. avoidance of litigation with regulatory agencies by identifying and correcting problems internally, and if the problem situation and proposed remedies are such that approval from regulatory agencies is needed, then being the initiator of such interaction and the proposer of alternative remedies will offer bargaining advantages.

4. notification to employees of the importance that corporate management attaches to compliance with environmental laws and regulations, increasing awareness of the seriousness of the waste management requirements, and making subsequent implementation of new or revised procedures and programs easier.

The following audit format has been developed for use with respect to waste management procedures. By following this step-by-step outline, a useful audit should result.

WASTE INVENTORY

The best place to start the audit is the waste inventory discussed in Chapter 3. A flow diagram of the plant operations and processes may also be prepared. Remember to prepare a list of inputs or raw materials used at the plant. Gather outside information about all raw materials, process chemicals, maintenance chemicals, etc., by requesting information from suppliers, i.e., obtaining material safety data sheets. Always use the assumption that what goes into the process will come out of the process.

For purposes of the inventory, assume any inputs exhibiting hazardous characteristics (from the material safety data sheet information) will need to be discarded. Although inputs are not normally discarded, possible reasons for their becoming wastes include:

1. expired shelf life;
2. inability to meet specifications;
3. damage, spoilage or contamination during storage;
4. discontinuation of the use of the input or manufacture of the associated product at the facility;
5. spills, leaks, ruptured containers or failure to keep the container closed, thereby allowing materials to set.

Prepare a list of wastes normally or occasionally generated by plant processes and operations.

1. Include process wastes, pollution control residuals, spent process chemicals, equipment maintenance wastes, by-products, off-specification outputs, etc.
2. For each waste, include other names for it, quantity generated per unit time, which process it is generated from and location.
3. Identify major components of each waste stream and potential contaminants. Use experience, common sense, good judgment, past analyses, and the material safety data sheets to do so.
4. Sample and analyze plant waste streams according to EPA protocols.

DETERMINATION OF HAZARDOUS WASTE

Determine which inputs, if discarded, are hazardous wastes according to the regulatory definitions. Consult the 261.33(e) and (f) (commercial chemical products) lists. The intention here is to identify materials that may need sampling and analysis if and when they are discarded.

Determine which wastes are hazardous according to the regulatory definitions:

1. Determine which wastes, if any, are excluded from regulation.
2. Determine if any wastes are listed in the regulations as hazardous (using the 261.31 and 261.32 lists).
3. For wastes that are not listed, each waste must be evaluated against the criteria for each characteristic [ignitability, corrosivity, reactivity, extraction procedure (EP) toxicity]. Determine, for each characteristic, whether the waste possesses that characteristic. This can be done by testing the waste, or by applying known information about the characteristics of the waste based on the process or materials used.

LISTS FOR BACKGROUND INFORMATION

By preparing the appropriate lists, the audit will provide the background information necessary to properly manage the various wastes in the future. These lists will also identify materials with reclamation potential, processes with large amounts of wastes and areas where input substitutions might be profitable. Using the format shown in Table X, or a similar format, prepare lists of hazardous wastes at the plant for:

1. inputs that, if discarded, are likely to be hazardous waste; and
2. waste streams that are occasionally or normally hazardous.

Table X.   Facility Hazardous Waste List

Waste Name
Hazardous Waste Number(s)
Hazard Code(s)
Process
Location
Physical State
Storage Method
Quantity Generated Per Unit Time

It is necessary to describe the physical state of the waste, e.g., color, pH, odor, consistency, solid, liquid or slurry. The type of storage used for the waste should also be given, e.g., drums, totes, roll-off container, bulk tank or waste pile. Remember that commercial chemical products listed in 261.33(e) or (f), if discarded, will have different hazardous waste numbers than the same chemical discarded after its intended use. A good example is solvents, some of which are listed in the 261.33 (f) and 261.31 lists. Which hazardous waste number applies depends on the point in the life cycle of the chemical at which it is discarded.

Prepare a second list of the nonhazardous industrial wastes at the plant (remember that these wastes may still be covered by state solid waste/industrial waste transporter regulations and U.S. Department of Transportation (DOT) regulations). Use the format shown in Table XI for these types of waste.

Table XI.   Facility Nonhazardous Waste List

Waste Name
Licensed Hauler Required?
Disposal Approval Required from State?
Process
Location
Physical State
Storage Method
Quantity Generated Per Unit Time

WASTE INFORMATION SHEET

For each waste stream (hazardous and nonhazardous) that has been identified, develop a waste information sheet. The preparation of the waste information sheet will require some reading and consultation of reference materials. Information sources include:

1. U.S. Environmental Protection Agency (EPA) regulations;
2. DOT regulations;
3. state regulatory agency;
4. disposal companies/transporters;
5. chemical manufacturers/vendors;
6. material safety data sheets; and
7. common chemical reference books.

The amount and type of information necessary for waste management purposes will depend on the material and the amount of handling/ treatment performed onsite. The types of information that may be useful include:

1. waste stream's common name;
2. hazardous waste number(s) and code(s);
3. reportable quantity (from 40 CFR 117) for spill-reporting purposes;
4. DOT shipping description and UN/NA number;
5. DOT hazard classes;
6. DOT container specification;
7. DOT labels and markings required;
8. disposal method and disposal facilities used;
9. transporter;
10. plant storage area to be used;
11. handling precautions;
12. health and safety considerations;
13. special handling equipment/worker protection required; and
14. toxicity rating (inhalation, dermal and oral).

SUPPLEMENTAL LISTS

Two supplemental lists should be attached to the waste information sheet for each waste stream—the "handling instruction sheet" and the "disposal instruction sheet." Together these lists form the core of a set of standard operating procedures to be developed to cover waste management at the facility. The information on each sheet will vary according to the waste and the level of specificity desired. Tables XII to XIV following give examples.

HAZARDOUS WASTE MANUAL

All of the information gathered, analytical results and the various lists will need to be organized. One way of doing so is to place the in-

Table XII.   Handling Instruction Sheet

Study the waste information sheet
Do not allow improper mixture of this waste with other wastes or materials
Keep away from heat or open flame
Use the safety equipment specified for the handling of this waste
Ensure that the waste is in the proper type of container
Properly label and mark each drum
Mark accumulation start date
Ensure that the container is closed tightly
Move drum to designated storage area
Record movement to storage in the operating record (if required)

Table XIII.   Disposal Instruction Sheet

Determine when to dispose (the end of the 90-day accumulation period or when a full load is accumulated)
Check for proper containerization
Check for leaks and closed containers
Check for proper labels and markings
Spot check to verify identity of waste materials (e.g., pH test, or visual inspection for color, odor, consistency)
Determine disposal method and disposal facility from the waste information sheet
Obtain written approvals from the disposal site and the state regulatory agency
Make the necessary arrangements with the disposal site and the transporter
Prepare the manifest according to manifest preparation sheet
Place manifest number on hazardous waste label
Check to see if the truck is properly placarded according to the load
Ship

---

formation materials in a three-ring binder. These materials can be organized in whatever way is most useful, given the amount of information involved. At this point, the following items have been prepared or obtained:

1. list of raw materials;
2. material safety data sheets for raw materials;
3. list of facility waste streams;
4. laboratory analyses on waste streams;
5. list of hazardous wastes: raw materials, if discarded and waste streams;
6. list of nonhazardous industrial wastes;
7. waste information sheets for each waste;
8. handling instruction sheets for each waste;
9. disposal instruction sheets for each waste; and

Table XIV.   Manifest Preparation Sheet

_____ Is the manifest document number on the manifest form? This number must be sequential with other manifest document numbers

_____ Name, address, phone number and EPA identification (ID) number of the generator/shipper

_____ Name, address, phone number and EPA ID number of the transporter/carrier

_____ Name, address, phone number and EPA ID number of the designated TSD facility

_____ Proper shipping description and classification (name, hazard class and UN/NA identification number); the word "waste" must precede the proper shipping name

_____ Quantity in weight or volume

_____ Number and type of containers

_____ EPA hazardous waste number

_____ Reportable quantity if amount of waste is above the reportable quantity

_____ National Response Center telephone number (1-800-424-8802) appears on the manifest

_____ Placards offered to transporter/carrier

_____ Special handling instructions on manifest (if necessary)

_____ Generator/shipper signature

_____ Transporter/carrier signature

_____ Generator copy of manifest retained and given to person responsible for manifest tracking

_____ Manifest sent with shipment

Completed by: _____name

_____title

_____date

Forward to: _____name

Reviewed by: _____name

10. manifest preparation sheet and any other standard operating procedures deemed necessary.

Another list to be developed for inclusion in the manual is that of the persons or companies that are involved in waste management matters. Phone numbers and names of contact persons should always be included. Examples are:

1. commercial treatment/disposal firms;
2. transportation companies;
3. consultants;
4. corporate environmental staff;

5. laboratories;
6. state environmental agencies;
7. federal regulatory agencies (EPA/DOT);
8. cleanup contractors;
9. emergency information sources such as Chemtrec; and
10. RCRA/Superfund hazardous waste hotline.

To fill out the manual, and to provide some information necessary later in the audit, certain items should be obtained from the state solid/ hazardous waste management agency:

1. a copy of the state enabling legislation for the hazardous waste management program;
2. a copy of the state hazardous waste management regulations;
3. a copy of any regulations regarding state licensing of hazardous waste transporters, and any list of licensed haulers;
4. a copy of any regulations, guidelines or procedures governing the use of state-permitted industrial or hazardous waste landfills and treatment facilities;
5. a list of approved commercial recycling, treatment and disposal sites in the state;
6. a list of waste exchanges operating in the state; and
7. any summaries of areas where the state regulatory program and regulations differ from the federal program and regulations.

EVALUATING THE EXISTING COMPLIANCE PROGRAM

Once the first part of the waste management audit is completed and procedures are set up to ensure proper management of all wastes from this point forward, the focus can shift to overall regulatory compliance.

Overall compliance with the federal and state solid and hazardous waste management requirements is different from merely identifying all wastes and providing for their proper treatment, storage or disposal (TSD). Such actions are no longer sufficient for compliance. The hazardous waste regulatory requirements imply a formal waste management program. A compliance program requires certain plans, records, procedures, reports and other documentation. The requirements of a compliance program depend on the regulatory category applicable to the firm's waste management activities. Determination of the applicable regulatory category was discussed in Chapter 5.

This second part of the waste management audit is to determine and understand the applicable regulatory requirements, and evaluate existing plant programs, practices, systems or procedures against the regulatory standards. The objective is to determine the degree of compliance and to identify areas of noncompliance. The regulatory standards explained in Section 2 for the various regulatory categories can be used as audit guidelines. The state hazardous waste laws, regulations and procedures need to be read and understood also. A mock inspection by the person performing the audit may be necessary to ascertain the degree of compliance with the federal and state requirements. The inspection form found in Appendix 5 may be used for this purpose.

DETERMINING PAST PRACTICES

The third part of the waste management audit is to determine how all of the various waste streams uncovered have been managed in the past. Looking through old records and questioning long-term employees or hauling/disposal contractors probably will be required. This information is necessary for several reasons, including:

1. notification of past hazardous waste disposal sites, required under Section 103(c) of the Comprehensive Environmental Response, Compensation, and Liability Act (CERCLA) of 1980 ("Superfund");
2. coverage of the past disposal sites under an environmental impairment liability policy; and
3. evaluation of the environmental risks and legal liabilities posed by past disposal practices.

Disposition of Wastes in the Past

Are the manufacturing processes and operations of the plant such that the same types of wastes have been generated since the plant was opened? If manufacturing processes and operations have changed, what were the previous types of wastes generated? Are there any records or indications as to the amounts of wastes generated/disposed of over the years? Where have these wastes been disposed of over the years? Have onsite disposal areas been used?

Status of Past Disposal Sites

Once the names of offsite disposal locations and the existence of any onsite activities have been uncovered, other actions become necessary. At this point, the information is probably vague (i.e., the "city dump" was used, or wastes were buried "out back"). It is necessary to physically locate and evaluate these sites, as there were probably several "city dumps" over the years. Relevant questions include:

1. Which disposal sites were used during various periods of plant operation?
2. What are the actual locations and present ownership of these sites?
3. Are any of the sites now closed or "abandoned"?
4. Was closure properly performed (i.e., at least 2 ft of final cover, proper grading and revegetation)?
5. Are any obvious problems present (e.g., exposed waste, continued dumping or leachate flowing offsite)?
6. Have the neighbors of any of these disposal sites been complaining about hazards in the area?
7. Offsite treatment/disposal facilities currently used should also be evaluated, as discussed in Chapter 18.

Remedial Actions

If there are any sites (on- or offsite) that pose immediate or potential environmental problems, it may be to the firm's advantage to secure the site itself. Doing so before governmental intervention may very well be cheaper and involve less adverse publicity than waiting for a court order. Perhaps a group of generators that used the site could contribute to the closure or remedial action costs.

POSTAUDIT PROCEDURES

Once the audit is completed, it is necessary to document the findings and lay out a set of recommendations that, if followed, would place the manufacturing facility in compliance and minimize the inherent risks and liabilities. At this point, plant management will decide which recommendations to accept and implement, and assign plant personnel to oversee their implementation.

The authors would like to emphasize the importance of the "waste managers" in the overall compliance program. The handling of hazardous wastes in accordance with the regulatory standards is largely a managerial exercise for manufacturing firms that store or accumulate hazardous waste. The person(s) responsible for waste management should have the knowledge, skills, motivation, authority and resources to do the job correctly. The "waste manager" should have sufficient communication skills (oral and written) to be able to prepare the necessary documentation, train other employees, and interact with regulatory officials, commercial hazardous waste management facilities and plant management.

CONCLUSIONS

An audit of past and present waste management practices will involve a good deal of effort if it is to serve its purposes. One of the more important purposes is to identify and correct any problems, so that future actions of the firm will be in full compliance with applicable laws and regulations. Complete compliance may not be achieved overnight. However, positive actions to solve any past problems or mistakes, and good faith efforts to comply with existing regulatory requirements will surely be viewed favorably by regulatory officials.

Chapter 17

DOCUMENTATION

The importance of a formal, well organized compliance program cannot be overstressed. It is no longer sufficient that a manufacturing firm merely manage its wastes properly. It is now necessary to document compliance. The purpose of this chapter is to provide a better understanding of the need for and benefits of the documentation portion of a compliance program.

A corporate compliance program necessarily implies paperwork. Paperwork includes preparation of plans; implementation of management systems and programs, and waste-handling standard operating procedures; keeping good records and compiling information in useful and reportable forms; documenting decisions, determinations and actions; and filing reports. Sections 1 and 2 outlined suggested and required paperwork necessary for a good waste management compliance program.

These suggestions and requirements should be used by waste management personnel at the firm to begin implementation of a compliance program, or to modify any existing procedures or programs. Of course, each manufacturing firm is unique in its production processes, layout and physical plant, organization of functions among employees, and other factors. The suggestions and examples given can and should be modified to meet the unique circumstances of each firm. However, the minimum regulatory requirements for each regulatory category must be met. Even so, some reordering of waste management activities may be possible to alter the applicable regulatory category.

Broadly speaking, the paperwork associated with a compliance program should not be viewed as unnecessary makework. It is useful to look at the paperwork associated with a compliance program as an insurance policy. In other words, by preparing plans and implementing procedures, and by documenting the decisions, determinations and

actions of the firm with respect to its hazardous waste management
a tivities, the risks and liabilities inherent to such activities are reduced
or minimized.

A formal, well organized compliance program will certainly make it
easier for regulatory agencies to ascertain compliance. Violation notices
or compliance orders, and the potential fines associated with noncompliance, can be avoided. The reporting aspects of such a program can
limit liabilities under the Resource Conservation and Recovery Act
(RCRA) and Comprehensive Environmental Response, Compensation
and Liability Act (CERCLA) of 1980 ("Superfund"). Hopefully, documentation requirements will encourage better decisions and make employees more conscious of how they handle waste materials.

There are other advantages to a compliance program. A program
that uses the guidance and suggestions in Chapters 14 and 15 can actually reduce waste management costs, or at least mitigate increases resulting from treatment/disposal price hikes. Further, a "house in order"
is a prerequisite to doing business with the more reputable commercial
hazardous waste management firms. Disposal of "unknowns" is at best
more expensive and difficult than disposal of segregated hazardous
wastes of known composition, and at worst is impossible. Finally, insurance companies will base the premiums (and availability) of comprehensive general liability and environmental impairment liability insurance at least partially on the quality of waste management practices
at the manufacturing facility under consideration.

The hazardous waste management regulations seem all paperwork
to waste management personnel at manufacturing firms. There are
waste analysis plans, contingency plans, operating records, inspection
logs, personnel training records, closure plans, manifest procedures,
and, of course, recordkeeping and reporting. That there is a substantial
amount of paperwork associated with compliance is beyond dispute.
The reasoning behind the paperwork is less obvious.

The author has come into contact with many people whose firms are
willing, even anxious, to manage their industrial wastes in a proper
manner. From their description of their waste management practices,
it seems they do. In other words, they have complied with the intent
and spirit of the law and some of the substantive aspects of the regulations, i.e., analysis of wastes, notification and permit application, inspections of the storage area, proper packaging, transportation under
manifest, and treatment/disposal at a facility under interim status.
However, some of these companies have not produced the paperwork
associated with compliance. Although they are on the right track, they
have yet to comply with both the spirit and letter of the requirements.

The rationale behind the "paperwork" requirements listed earlier is to document that some thought has gone into the sampling and analysis of wastes, the necessary reactions to emergency situations, the content and frequency of inspections, the content and extent of training, etc. The "paperwork" requirements also document that certain activities have been carried out, or followed through.

The inspector has no recourse other than to rely on such documentation in the evaluation of the extent of compliance with certain of the regulatory requirements. Indeed, a review of the documentation (including records) is the only way an evaluation can be made for some of the requirements.

In summary, the documentation ("paperwork") required by regulation is indeed necessary and vital to the manufacturing firm interested in complying with hazardous waste management regulations. Instead of viewing such requirements as busywork, they can perhaps be more profitably perceived as opportunities to rethink old methods of waste management, to reduce risks and liabilities, to plan for emergencies, to develop written standard operating procedures, to eliminate substandard practices, and to pursue new directions in industrial processes and waste management methods that will help the firm achieve compliance in a least-cost fashion. Viewed in this manner, these "paperwork" requirements are not nearly as burdensome. Indeed, they become part and parcel of enlightened industrial management.

SECTION 4

SELECTED CONSIDERATIONS IN IMPLEMENTING A HAZARDOUS WASTE MANAGEMENT PROGRAM

Onsite accumulation or storage of hazardous wastes before offsite treatment or disposal is largely a managerial exercise. As a result, there are many aspects of industrial waste management that cannot be described in regulations. An understanding of some of these aspects usually is gained only through experience. The purpose of this section is to provide the reader with some guidance in these areas. It is hoped that this guidance will prove useful to waste managers, and will help them avoid some of the more common problems and pitfalls.

Chapter 18

SELECTING AN OFFSITE TREATMENT OR DISPOSAL FACILITY

Finding and selecting a treatment or disposal facility that is (1) competently managed, (2) in compliance with the applicable regulatory standards, and (3) in possession of the permits, equipment and expertise necessary to handle a particular waste are crucial to corporate compliance and limitation of liability. However, the regulations do not provide much guidance to that end, nor will regulatory agencies recommend any one firm over others under interim status.

Matters are further complicated by the fact that many commercial hazardous waste management facilities offer only one waste management technology (e.g., disposal, chemical treatment or incineration); this limits the types of wastes they will accept. This is a problem when there are several types of wastes at a manufacturing facility, each requiring different waste management methods or a different sequence of methods. Additionally, some wastes can be handled properly by more than one method. Finally, some commercial hazardous waste management facilities will accept all types of hazardous wastes, but can perform only one (or a few) waste management operation(s) onsite. The wastes they cannot handle onsite will often be "brokered" to another commercial hazardous waste firm. These brokerage facilities can legally accept such wastes and sign and return a copy of the manifest to the generator. However, the return of the manifest to the generator does not, in this case, signify that the material has been managed as promised (by disposal, incineration or recycling). The return of the manifest may only mean that the wastes have been put into long-term storage, representing a potential liability should the broker accepting the waste go out of business.

The purpose of this chapter is to provide some guidance in the choice of whether to do business with a particular commercial hazardous waste management firm. It is assumed that there has been a decision as to which method(s) are appropriate for the waste stream in question. The decision between waste management technologies is waste-specific and largely technical. However, the decision to deal with a particular commercial treatment, storage or disposal (TSD) facility is only partially based on the equipment and techniques or methods available there. The nontechnical elements of selection are to be discussed shortly.

One further preliminary warning is necessary. There are commercial TSD facilities under interim status that have little chance of meeting the standards necessary to obtain a full Resource Conservation and Recovery Act (RCRA) permit. These facilities will close or change hands shortly after Part B of their RCRA permit application is requested by the U.S. Environmental Protection Agency (EPA) or the state. It is necessary to keep this in mind when dealing with commercial TSD facilities, and to be especially cautious until all such facilities have full RCRA permits.

The key component of the hazardous waste management system is the responsibility of the generator for the disposition and environmental impact of his hazardous wastes. Given this responsibility, it is imperative to do business only with commercial TSD facilities that will minimize the risk of future liability claims on your company. The legal liabilities and statutory and common law responsibilities of manufacturing firms as hazardous waste generators are discussed in Chapter 22.

There are several areas by which the "quality" of a particular commercial hazardous waste management firm can be evaluated. These areas are permits, physical plant, management and personnel, housekeeping and operations, insurance, and compliance status.

PERMITS

Is the facility in possession of a valid EPA Identification Number? Ask to see a copy of the "Acknowledgement of Notification of Hazardous Waste Activity" (EPA Form 8700-12A) sent to the facility by the EPA.

Has the facility filed Part A of the federal consolidated permit application (EPA forms 3510-1 and 3510-3)? Ask to see a copy and verify that the application includes both the specific type(s) of wastes you wish to be managed at the facility and the process code(s) for the waste management method(s) you desire to use.

If the facility involves a wastewater discharge, ask to see a copy of its National Pollutant Discharge Elimination System (NPDES) permit (for discharge to navigable waterways) or municipal pretreatment permit or letter of approval (for discharge to municipal sewer systems).

Inquire as to possession of all necessary state permits (e.g., state sanitary landfill permit or state hazardous waste management facility permit). Review such permits for design life (important for landfills), operating capacity, and any permit conditions or restrictions on capacity that could affect the ability of the facility to promptly process your wastes. In addition, verify what can and cannot be handled at the facility. Of importance are the specific restrictions (e.g., no liquid wastes, no chlorinated wastes or no heavy metal wastes).

Get copies of all permits, including any air pollution and wastewater discharge permits. Does each waste stream or waste shipment need prior written approval (a "permit letter" or "approval letter") from the state regulatory agency?

PHYSICAL PLANT

Tour the facility. Look at and verify the existence and working condition of any processing equipment described in promotional literature. Observe the general housekeeping. Determine the types and amounts of security, emergency and spill control equipment. Are emergency instructions posted? Are there sufficient alarms and communication equipment?

Look at waste storage areas. Is all drum storage conducted on concrete pads with curbs and collection sumps? Ask what is done with the spills, leaks, and precipitation collected in the sump. Is there diking around all storage tanks? Look for nearby spill control equipment at the areas where drums are off-loaded, where drums are pumped, and where any drums are staged for shipment offsite.

Landfills and facilities with surface impoundments require special attention. Does the facility have a liner (synthetic membrane or re-compacted clay)? Does the facility have a functional leachate collection and removal system? What is done with the collected leachate? Does the facility have the required groundwater monitoring system? Has the facility submitted the monitoring results to the appropriate regulatory agencies? What is the disposition of stormwater runon and runoff? Does the discharge from any holding pond have a NPDES permit?

For landfills it is necessary to inquire as to the disposal method. Are hazardous wastes codisposed with municipal refuse, or disposed of with other hazardous wastes? The author must admit to a bias against codisposal of hazardous wastes with municipal wastes, especially for wastes that are hazardous by virtue of heavy metal content.

Is there a laboratory onsite? A modern, well equipped laboratory is a necessity for hazardous waste treatment facilities. Hazardous waste landfills should have sufficient laboratory capabilities to verify ("fingerprint") by a few tests that the wastes received are the same type as they agreed to accept. Properly staffed laboratories at treatment facilities should not only have "fingerprinting" capabilities, but should be able to completely analyze the wastes, the treated effluent, and any residues and sludges from treatment. Inquire as to the existence of quality control programs for the laboratory procedures and equipment.

MANAGEMENT AND PERSONNEL

It is necessary to evaluate the qualifications of facility personnel and their ability to properly run a business in the complex and highly regulated field of hazardous waste management. Credentials (university degrees) are nice, but training and experience in hazardous waste management or related fields (chemical manufacture, wastewater treatment) are better. An intimate knowledge of regulatory requirements is a must. Inquire as to the quality of the training program for employees, and its regularity. Does training include emergency control and spill response training? Are workers provided with safety equipment? Observe the familiarity of key personnel with the actual day-to-day operations of the facility. Are they effectively overseeing operations, or merely letting things slide? The elements of this category are not easily evaluated, but the quality of the firm in terms of management and personnel is one of the more important factors in the choice of which firm to deal with.

HOUSEKEEPING AND OPERATIONS

This category is relatively easy to observe and evaluate. Although it applies primarily to treatment, recycling and incineration operations, the suggestions and questions below have some applicability to landfills. Observe the general level of housekeeping, especially around offloading and waste transfer (pumping) areas. Watch the workers' waste handling practices. Are the workers wearing protective clothing and equipment? Do they appear cautious? Are they causing sloppy conditions? Are there written material-handling and spill-prevention and -control procedures?

Although the larger, well run treatment and recycling operations use bulk (tank) storage and transportation almost exclusively, there will likely be some drum storage. Observe the conditions of drum storage. Are the drums on a concrete pad? Are they stacked more than two high and two wide for a row? Do they appear excessively aged (i.e., are the drums weathered, rusty, leaking, or damaged; have the labels and markings faded or fallen off)? Does there seem to be an excessive inventory for facility operations? Does the inventory consist of wastes that cannot be handled onsite (either "brokered" wastes or wastes generated by the facility itself)? To which facilities do "brokered" wastes go? How are wastes generated by facility operations (process residues, sludges, cooling water, wastewaters) managed, and where? Does the inventory consist of "product" (reclaimed solvents or oils) awaiting sale? Does the firm have a steady market for any reclaimed products?

INSURANCE

Under the broad heading of insurance come the considerations of the financial stability of the firm, and its ability to pay for the responsibilities associated with a hazardous waste management facility. These responsibilities include:

1. proper closure of the facility at any time;
2. postclosure monitoring and maintenance (for disposal sites);
3. the ability to compensate injured parties for claims arising from facility operations that accidentally injure persons or property.

All facilities must have compensatory capabilities with respect to sudden and accidental occurrences (fires, explosions or releases). Surface impoundments and disposal facilities must, in addition, have such capabilities for gradual and accidental occurrences (such as groundwater contamination).

A firm that has the financial strength and the financial instruments (such as trust funds and insurance policies) to meet the costs associated with closure and accidents will protect the generators using the site from claims against the commercial TSD facility. The legal liabilities of manufacturing facilities as generators and users of offsite TSD facilities is discussed in Chapter 22.

The federal regulations [40 CFR 265, Subpart H, 47 FR 15032] require owners or operators of hazardous waste management facilities to estimate the cost of closure (and postclosure care, if applicable). Owners or operators of such facilities are to establish financial responsibility for these costs through:

1. trust fund,
2. letter of credit,
3. surety bond,
4. financial test, or
5. insurance policy providing funds for closure or postclosure care.

These requirements are effective July 6, 1982.

The federal regulations [40 CFR 265, Subpart H, 47 FR 16544] also require hazardous waste facility owners or operators to demonstrate liability coverage for bodily injury and property damage to third parties resulting from facility operations.

For sudden accidental occurrences resulting from facility operations, liability insurance in minimum amounts of $1 million per occurrence and $2 million annual aggregate (exclusive of legal defense costs) is required. The effective date for the sudden accidental liability coverage is July 15, 1982. A certificate of insurance or other evidence of coverage for sudden accidental occurrences must be submitted to EPA (and the relevant state) by this date. It is of interest to note that this type of coverage is often obtained through comprehensive general liability policies.

Surface impoundments and disposal facilities are, in addition, required to have coverage for gradual accidents. For gradual accidental occurrences, coverage for claims is required in the amounts of $3 million per occurrence, $6 million annual aggregate, again exclusive of legal defense costs. The requirements for this type of coverage are being phased in. Owner/operators with annual sales or revenues of $10 million or more will be required to submit evidence of gradual accident coverage by January 16, 1983. Those with annual sales or revenues of $5–10 million are required to submit evidence of nonsudden coverage by January 16, 1984. All other TSD facilities requiring this coverage must submit evidence of it by January 16, 1985.

A company may demonstrate compliance with the liability requirements by obtaining the required insurance policy(ies) or by meeting the specified financial test, or some combination of the two.

This brief outline of the federal financial responsibility requirements makes possible a knowledgeable review of commercial TSD documentation. It is important to determine whether and how the facility has provided for closure (and postclosure, if applicable) financial burdens. Find out which of the mechanisms have been used for this requirement.

With regard to the liability insurance policy, it will be necessary to get a copy of the facility's certificate of insurance for sudden occurrences. Verify that coverage with the issuing insurance firm. For landfills or surface impoundments, inquire as to the existence of coverage for gradual occurrences. Even though the facility may not legally be required to have the coverage at this time, it is advisable to deal only with a TSD that has demonstrated the ability to obtain nonsudden insurance, or that has the financial strength to meet the financial test for self-insurance. Financial responsibility for TSD facilities is discussed further in Chapter 23.

COMPLIANCE STATUS

The evaluation of a commercial facility's compliance status begins at the facility itself, and ends with a verification of those findings with the appropriate federal and state regulatory officials.

While on a tour of the facility, ask to see a copy of the facility's contingency plan. Does it cover the types of emergencies most likely to happen at the facility? Ask the whereabouts of the primary emergency coordinator listed in the contingency plan.

Ask to see a copy of the facility's latest interim status standards inspection by federal or state hazardous waste facility inspectors. Review the inspection form and the accompanying letter (called a notice of violation or compliance order) for major deficiencies noted by the inspector. Ask to see the facility's written response to the inspection, which should note the actions the facility took to come into compliance. Verify that such actions were actually performed.

At this point it is necessary to review the history of the site, first with facility personnel and then with regulatory officials. Are there any notice of violation letters or compliance orders for which a written response and appropriate remedial actions have not been performed? Are there any enforcement actions pending against the facility? Has the facility ever been taken to court to obtain compliance with environmental regulations? Is the site operating under an agreed order or consent decree? Is the facility in environmental receivership? Are there any court-issued orders relating to a lack of progress in meeting the terms of compliance orders, agreed orders, or consent decrees?

After completion of the facility tour, it is necessary to verify your findings and the completeness of any statements by facility personnel.

This is best done by a visit to the state regulatory agency's office. Make an appointment with the field inspector for the facility in question. Arrive early and examine the agency's file(s) on the facility. Remember that the facility may have a NPDES (water pollution) permit also. After reviewing the files, meet with the facility inspector. Verify that the facility is in possession of, or has applied for the necessary permits. Explore any questions or problem areas that were raised as a result of your facility tour. Review the compliance status and history of the site, as told you by the facility personnel.

Other items need to be verified through conversation with the inspector or through review of the files. Is the facility "brokering" any unprocessed wastes from generators to another TSD? Where are "brokered" wastes sent? Do these facilities have the necessary permits? What is the disposition of any leachates, cooling waters or process waters? Do any discharges need permits? Are there restrictions on the types of wastes the facility may accept? What types of wastes is the facility permitted to accept? Do waste streams or waste shipments need any approval from the state regulatory agency? Has the facility filed evidence of compliance with state financial responsibility requirements for closure and postclosure, and sudden and gradual liability insurance? If the facility is a landfill or a surface impoundment, has it submitted the required groundwater monitoring results? Do these results indicate any groundwater contamination?

The final subject to broach with the state inspector is one for which you may not get a direct answer. Inspectors are told not to recommend facilities. However, ask his opinion of the facility. Is it well run compared to similar facilities? What is its reputation with the state and with its customers? Do not expect a recommendation to use any one facility over others, or any glittering evaluations.

Read between the lines, remembering that it is an inspector's job to find faults and ensure that the facility meets the regulatory standards.

TSD FACILITY REQUIREMENTS OF GENERATORS

It is important to note that well run firms will be as choosy about dealing with you as you should be with them. These commercial facilities will not accept any and all hazardous wastes, as doing so could put them in violation of their permit as well as potentially causing immediate (fires, explosions) or future (groundwater contamination) problems at their facility. Well run commercial firms will require you to fill out forms giving detailed information about the waste and the processes that generated it. They will require analyses and samples of the wastes, and certifications by the generator regarding the accuracy of the information and the nature of the wastes shipped to the site. Keep a file of all your dealings with a particular firm, including the results of the facility tour.

TSD FACILITY REEVALUATION

Once you begin doing business with a commercial firm, it is necessary to periodically reevaluate the facility and verify the actual disposition of the manufacturing firm's wastes. It is important to find out what actually happened to each shipment of waste to the facility. Was the waste immediately processed (treated, incinerated or landfilled)? Has the waste been placed in storage [in the original container or in bulk (tank) storage]? Has the waste been brokered to another firm, or is it awaiting approval (from the state or from the other TSD) to be brokered? Determine the processing or "turnaround" time for your type of waste. This is the time the wastes sit in storage before treatment or disposal. In general, the shorter the processing time the better the facility is run, and the lesser the generator's exposure to liability from incidents that may occur during storage.

Many firms offer a certificate of disposal verifying the time and date that the waste was actually processed (treated, incinerated or landfilled). This certificate of disposal is in addition to a signed manifest. The receipt of a signed manifest from the designated TSD facility really only signifies that the facility has received and accepts the wastes specified on the manifest. The receipt of a signed manifest does not mean that the designated facility actually processed the wastes as agreed on before shipment.

CONCLUSION

There are many elements to evaluate in selecting an offsite TSD facility to do business with. This chapter has only brought up some of the more relevant questions to ask and things to determine or evaluate. No weights have been assigned to these matters, and thus the decision to use a particular facility cannot be as simple as assigning each possible facility a "score." Further, no mention has been made of the price of a commercial firm's services. To a great extent, the old adage that "you get what you pay for" is true in this decision. Waste management personnel at manufacturing firms will need to apply their own decision rules, assign their own priorities, and use good judgment and common sense in making the very important decision of which offsite firm(s) to use.

Chapter 19

PRINCIPLES OF HAZARDOUS WASTE STORAGE

Hazardous waste storage in a safe and proper manner is not an intrinsically difficult task. The principles are amazingly simple. The reason hazardous waste storage is often not conducted properly is ignorance of the minimum regulatory requirements and a lack of forethought regarding how to perform storage. In the past this lack of thought has resulted from the secondary nature of wastes in a manufacturing operation. Wastes were primarily viewed as unwanted and inevitable by-products of production, to be gotten rid of with a minimum of cost, time and effort.

The regulations that came about partially as a result of these past improper storage (and disposal) practices have been discussed earlier in this book. This chapter will only refer briefly to the standards as they apply to onsite accumulation (Chapter 10) and storage (Chapter 11). The bulk of this chapter is an attempt to bring together these regulatory standards with the common sense, basic chemical knowledge and good practices involved in the safe and proper storage of hazardous wastes. At a minimum, this involves handling wastes with at least the same degree of care and consideration given the virgin input chemicals used at the manufacturing facility. Of course, these input chemicals are often major constituents of manufacturing wastes.

CONTAINERIZATION

The first principle of hazardous waste storage is to place waste stored in containers on an impermeable base. This will make cleanup of any spills or leaks much easier and cheaper, since there will be no contaminated soil to dispose of, and the possibilities of soil and groundwater contamination are minimized. The storage base or pad is usually poured concrete. The pad should not be dissolved or deteriorated by spills or leaks, as asphalt would be by spilled solvents. There should be provisions for collecting any spills and leaks, without their draining uncontrolled to a plant or city sewer.

Ideally, the storage area should be curbed or diked to collect spills, leaks and precipitation. The curb or dike should be "keyed" into or otherwise sealed at the base to adequately contain liquids. The curb should be high enough to contain a volume of liquid equal to 10% of the volume of the maximum inventory of containers, or the volume of the largest container, whichever is greater. The base should be sloped to a central collection area or sump, to minimize contact between liquids and the containers. The storage pad should not be located in a 100-yr flood plain. If an existing drum accumulation or storage area is to be modified to meet these guidelines, it is suggested that the 40 CFR 264 permit standards for storage in containers be consulted [46 FR 2866 and 55112]. Although the Part 264 permit standards do not apply to accumulation areas, they can serve as guidelines. At some time in the future, circumstances may make it necessary to pursue a permit for what is now an accumulation area.

PROTECTION FROM WEATHER

The second principle of storage is that the wastes should be provided some protection from the elements. In other words, storage should be under a roof, either inside the manufacturing facility, in a separate building for the storage of input chemicals and/or wastes, or underneath a pole barn or three-sided shed.

Although the primary concern is to prevent the possibility of precipitation being a conduit for contamination of surrounding areas, there are other concerns. The movement of waste containers becomes nearly impossible when they are surrounded by snow and ice. Further, some wastes should not be exposed to direct sunlight (especially in black drums) or should be protected from freezing. Exposure to the elements will weather the waste container and the required markings and labels. Remember, however, to provide adequate ventilation of any enclosed areas.

WASTE SEGREGATION

The third principle of hazardous waste storage is to segregate wastes that have incompatible chemical properties. Segregation can be accomplished by waste type or hazard classification. Incompatible drummed wastes are to be separated by means of a dike, berm, wall or other device [265.177]. When a manufacturing facility has two (or more) waste streams that are incompatible, the drums should be very clearly marked, perhaps even color-coded. Additionally, the specific areas within the storage facility where such wastes are to be stored should be clearly designated, by signs and/or markings on the floor. Appendix V of 40 CFR 265 provides examples of waste categories that are incompatible, as well as the potential consequences should such wastes come in contact with each other. Further information is found in the EPA publication "A Method for Determining the Compatibility of Hazardous Wastes" (EPA-600/2-80-076).

STORAGE AREA LOCATION

The fourth principle has to do with the location of the storage area(s) within the property controlled by the manufacturing facility. The primary constraints have to do with the safety of workers, equipment and structures should there be a fire or explosion, or should incompatible wastes come into contact. Storage areas where ignitable, reactive or incompatible wastes are held should be readily accessible to internal emergency personnel (fire brigades) as well as to emergency response organizations that might be called on to provide emergency services. Storage areas for such wastes should be separated from plant operations. Sometimes explosion-proof rooms are constructed to protect workers and equipment. Changing the physical location of waste accumulation or storage areas within the facility's premises may have beneficial insurance consequences, so consult with the insurance carrier and their safety experts. Remember the regulatory constraint that ignitables or reactives cannot be stored closer to the property line than 50 ft [265.176].

STORAGE AREA ARRANGEMENT

The fifth principle has to do with the arrangement of the waste storage area itself, so as to provide accessibility. Accessibility is required for various purposes. Since many offsite TSD facilities can accept only one type of waste (e.g., solvents, acids or heavy metal sludges), drums of the particular waste type at the manufacturing facility must be identified easily and accessed for removal to the offsite TSD. In addition, the drums must be inspected weekly for leaks or corrosion [265.174], and adequate aisle space must be maintained for unobstructed movement of personnel and equipment [265.35]. These two regulatory requirements have been translated into the practice of storing waste containers in rows that are two high and two wide. Each row should have sufficient aisle space to allow access.

Aisles can be painted on the storage pad, along with areas where rows of drums of a particular waste type are to be stored. Remember that incompatible wastes are to be separated by a dike, berm, wall or other device [265.177].

Arrangement of wastes in this manner will make it easier to comply with the operating record requirements. The operating record must contain "the location of each hazardous waste within the facility and the quantity at each location" [265.73(b)(2)]. This requirement can be satisfied by showing the number of drums of each type of waste in storage at their accurate locations on a sketch of the floor plan of the storage area. This sketch should be drawn to scale; the grid lines of graph paper on the sketch would be helpful guides for showing accurate waste locations. This sketch would need to be modified as wastes are moved into storage and a new sketch made as wastes are shipped offsite for treatment and/or disposal.

Other considerations and practices related to storing hazardous wastes cannot be elevated to the level of first principles, but are provided here in the form of suggestions.

STORAGE IN TANKS

Storage in bulk (in tanks) is usually practical only for manufacturers with large amounts of waste materials. Bulk storage can also be used for semisolid materials, as when wastewater treatment sludges are stored temporarily in roll-off containers of multiple cubic yard capacity. For those manufacturers for whom bulk storage is not feasible, there are several practices that can lower the cost of drum storage.

STORAGE IN DRUMS

Storage of hazardous wastes in 55-gal containers (often called drums or barrels) is really a second-best method. Storage in drums (as opposed to bulk storage in tanks) has several drawbacks. The per-unit (weight or volume) costs of treatment and/or disposal are inevitably higher when the wastes are managed in drums. This is because of costs associated with manipulating wastes in containers. In addition, unit transportation costs are higher for containerized wastes. Finally, the cost of the drum itself must be factored into overall costs. Disposal facilities bury the wastes in the drum, and treatment facilities rarely return empty drums. The cost of a new drum is $23–28, while reconditioned drums run $14–21. If the drums in which input materials are shipped are used for disposal purposes, then any deposit on the drum is forfeited. If there was no deposit, the money a barrel reclaimer would have paid for an empty drum is foregone.

New drums should not be used routinely for waste storage or transportation. Reclaimed drums meeting U.S. Department of Transportation (DOT) specifications are available at lower cost from barrel reclaimers. In addition, it is sometimes permissible to put waste materials back into the drum in which they were transported as raw material. However, find the markings on the drum itself and check the DOT regulations to see whether reuse is permissible. Reuse of containers in transportation is governed by DOT regulations, including those set forth at 49 CFR 173.28.

Drums should be stored on pallets, if possible, to minimize corrosion and contact with precipitation, spills or leaks. Some waste managers move drums on pallets, instead of individually. Mechanical devices are available that can be attached to forklifts to make the movement and loading of 55-gal drums fairly simple.

Transfer of wastes from container to container should be kept to an absolute minimum. This will minimize the inevitable leaks, drips and spills that accompany the handling of uncontainerized waste. A good way to cut down on pumping or scooping wastes from one container to another is by using a container suitable for offsite transportation to initially contain the waste. This means, typically, using a 55-gal barrel meeting DOT specifications for the type of waste material to be containerized.

Because waste-handling operations are often accompanied by spills and leaks, it is important to have some sort of absorbent material readily available. Commonly used absorbents include cement kiln dust, fly ash, oil dry and expanded clay. Some of the new synthetic absorbent media are especially effective and easy to use.

Some form of internal labeling system can be very helpful in complying with the regulations and keeping a handle on various types of wastes generated at the facility. Generators who accumulate must, of course, mark each drum of hazardous waste with the words "hazardous waste" and the accumulation start date (Figure 5). The start date is the date that the first drop of waste is placed in the container. Although not

Figure 5.   Accumulation start date label (courtesy Labelmaster).

strictly required, other information could be placed on a decal to be attached to the drum. Such information could include the generator's
name; the waste's common name; the hazard(s) posed by the waste;
the department, process or machine generating the waste; the date; and
a reminder to workers to keep the container closed when wastes are not
being added. Some companies might also want to provide a place for
the signature of the waste coordinator. His signature would be necessary before a drum could be moved to an accumulation or storage area.
This allows the coordinator to keep track of the types and amounts of
waste in storage, makes segregation of waste streams easier, and keeps
half-full drums from being moved to storage. This also provides a
check on employees using hazardous waste containers as garbage cans.
Labels are available that will identify barrels containing nonhazardous
wastes, as well as for "empty" containers (Figure 6).

A system of color-coded drums could be used to supplement the internal labels. Each waste stream would be assigned a specific color
drum. White or light-colored drums should be used for ignitable wastes
or volatile (high-vapor-pressure) liquids. The use of light-colored
drums for such wastes is important if wastes are stored outside. Under
no circumstances should ignitable or flammable wastes be placed in
black drums and exposed to direct sunlight.

Labeling and marking of containers is a regulatory requirement of
generators before they can offer their wastes to a transporter for movement offsite (Chapter 12). This requirement raises the issue of when
such containers should be properly labeled and marked—at the time
the container is placed in storage or just before loading for offsite TSD.
Although the regulations require the proper labels and markings before

Figure 6.   Sample waste container labels for in-house use (courtesy Labelmaster).

transporting or offering hazardous waste for transportation offsite, and this has been interpreted to mean just before loading, a good case can be made for proper labeling and marking when the container is moved to an accumulation area or placed in storage.

One of the primary reasons for early labeling and marking is to give the workers handling the waste information regarding the type of material they are handling, and its hazard classification. This information is necessary for them to be safety-conscious while handling the wastes. This will also give them basic information necessary to respond to a spill or fire. Another persuasive argument is that the day the transporter shows up to take the wastes to the offsite TSD is likely to be very hectic. The manifest must be completed, the drums checked for tight lids and bungs, deterioration, or leaks. Further, it is likely that the TSD will only accept certain types of the wastes present. Those drums must be located and staged for loading onto the truck. A semi-trailer can hold up to 80 drums. To have to properly label and mark large numbers of drums with an impatient trucker waiting is not the most pleasant task.

The author contends that the labeling and marking necessary for off-site transportation are best done as the wastes are moved to accumulation areas or onsite storage facilities. This will prevent the container from becoming an "unknown" (especially if an internal labeling system is not used), requiring costly analysis to reestablish the identity of the contents. This practice will also allow segregation of wastes and keeping an operating record (required for TSD facilities at 265.73).

If the drums are stored outside of a building, there can be problems with labels fading, peeling or washing off. This is not an insoluble problem. Weather-resistant labels (usually vinyl) are available (Figure 7). Indelible ink pens or spray paint and stencils also work well.

The final consideration to be covered is that of the amounts of wastes to be kept in storage. Waste storage should be kept at "reasonable" levels. This presents little problem to the small-quantity generator or the generator who must move wastes offsite within 90 days. For generators who have a TSD storage facility, "reasonable" levels could be thought of as less than truckload quantity levels. The number of "truckloads" present will depend on how many different commercial treatment and/or disposal sites are necessary for the types of wastes generated at the manufacturing facility. It should be emphasized that the prices of offsite treatment or disposal are going to continue to rise faster than inflation, so stockpiling will not save money. Stockpiling ignitable or reactive wastes just increases risks and will cause concern with the firm's insurance carrier.

Figure 7. Exterior-grade vinyl waste container labels (courtesy Label-master).

It is hoped that the principles and common sense hints contained in this chapter will prove useful to manufacturing firms currently using improper storage practices. All too often in the past wastes have been put in deteriorated containers, without bungs, lids or markings. These containers were then placed on bare soil or gravel areas for indefinite periods. Great progress has been made in upgrading storage practices, but some improvement is still necessary for wastes to be accumulated or stored in a safe and proper manner.

Chapter 20

DEALING WITH REGULATORY PERSONNEL

Jack Cornpropst

    VonDuprin Division of Schlage Lock
    Ingersoll-Rand Corporation
    Indianapolis, Indiana

This chapter discusses dealing with people from governmental regulatory agencies, from the viewpoint of an electroplater and licensed industrial wastewater treatment operator.

Electroplating and other surface-finishing operations seem to be the subject of close government scrutiny and regulation. Much of this attention is understandable, due to the nature of surface-finishing operations and the types of materials and process chemicals used in such operations. Part of being a good electroplater is to properly manage the solid and liquid wastes resulting from electroplating and industrial wastewater treatment operations. In other words, one is not only an electroplater, but also an industrial "garbage man." By properly managing a company's wastes, one fulfills an important corporate and personal responsibility.

It is obvious that for all government regulatory programs to succeed, there must be a high degree of voluntary compliance on the part of the regulated industries. There simply are not enough governmental employees or enough jail cells available, were there to be any significant degree of resistance to such programs. For the most part, there is no basic disagreement between government and industry on the goals of clean air, clean water, a safe workplace, and control of toxic and hazardous materials and wastes.

The best way, and perhaps the only way that the national hazardous waste program can be as successful as we wish it to be is through development of a spirit of cooperation between industry and governmental authorities. This cooperation is necessary for voluntary compliance. Of course, enforcement and fines should be reserved for those that fail to comply with substantive aspects of the regulations and/or fail to make good faith efforts to comply with paperwork requirements. Industry wants fair and reasonable enforcement; otherwise, the companies in compliance compete against firms that do not bear the very real costs of compliance.

A cooperative approach will alleviate the stresses associated with compliance efforts during a confrontation with a government agency. Cooperation, though, is a two-way street. There are certain things that industry can expect of the state environmental agency (i.e., the state board of health, the state department of natural resources, or the state environmental protection agency) and there are those things that the state agency can expect of industry.

Industry should be able to expect some advance notice of new environmental regulations, and the opportunity to comment on such regulations before they take effect. This is far better than to have to try to get unworkable regulations changed after they are finalized. Also, industry should be able to readily obtain interpretations of federal and state environmental regulations. It is not always perfectly obvious what is required, even after several readings of the *Federal Register*. Also, the regulations should be consistently and fairly applied. I think that industry can reasonably expect the state environmental agency to make an attempt to understand general (industrywide) problems and specific (one plant or firm) problems or situations. Finally, there should be some way or mechanism available for a company to discuss compliance problems with the state agency without fear of a citation or reprisal.

As I said before, cooperation is a two-way street. For state environmental personnel to be able to understand the compliance problems of a certain industry or firm, they must be allowed to become familiar with the particular processes and operations involved. Company personnel should cooperate as fully as possible with inspectors. This includes access to the property, an explanation of production processes and operations, complete answers to questions, and access to relevant records and information. Also, the state agency should be able to expect diligent, good faith efforts to comply with the requirements. Finally, problems that may affect others, such as spills or leaks to waterways, should be reported immediately. This includes bringing "skeletons out of the closet," so that the situation can be addressed before any serious environmental impacts result (i.e., proper closure of any old company dumps).

Company waste managers should read the applicable regulations and make an attempt to understand them. Questions on the applicability of certain requirements or on the correctness of a particular interpretation of a "grey area" should be resolved before any deadlines have passed. Ignorance of the law should not be used as an excuse, nor should the lame response that "others are doing it."

This cooperation usually begins and develops at the lowest involvement level, i.e., between a company's hazardous waste manager and the state inspector. This cooperation is based on the realization that both parties have a job to do and that both are accountable to superiors. Further, the company's waste manager and the inspector are not (or should not be) on opposite sides of the fence. In fact, they have similar objectives. The objective of the hazardous waste manager at the company is to properly handle and dispose of the hazardous wastes resulting from company activities. The objective of the hazardous waste inspector is to verify that proper waste management is actually being performed at the facility, in accordance with the applicable laws and regulations.

With a realization of these similar objectives, each party must make an effort to understand and assist and offer encouragement with the other's problems. Both the inspector and the waste manager possess specialized information, knowledge and experiences that could be beneficially used by the other.

Of course, there is always the possibility of encountering an individual with whom the development of a working relationship is impossible. Fortunately, such persons are not frequently encountered. All one can do is to make sure that all statements made (both oral and written) are absolutely correct, be firm in one's convictions and hope for the best.

To summarize, the hazardous waste management laws and regulations are lengthy and complex. Whether any company could ever be in complete compliance, at all times, with the letter of the regulations is questionable. Given these premises and the accountability of industrial "garbage men" to corporate management, the author contends that cooperation with regulatory agencies is the only workable alternative. The hazardous waste management system is still relatively new. Both industry and government are learning to implement and fine-tune their respective programs. With the right attitude and recognition of their respective responsibilities, a workable and effective system can result.

Chapter 21

WHAT TO EXPECT
DURING AN INSPECTION

All manufacturing firms that notified the U.S. Environmental Protection Agency (EPA) of hazardous waste activity should expect to be inspected periodically for compliance with the regulatory standards. Manufacturing firms that submitted an application ("Part A") for a hazardous waste permit should expect to be inspected with greater frequency than firms that accumulate less than 90 days. Inspections are also performed on facilities that are the subject of a complaint, or that are suspected of flagrant violations or of not notifying or submitting a permit application.

The inspection will typically be conducted by an employee of the state agency with regulatory authority for hazardous waste management. Appendix 2 gives for all states the name of the agency with such authority. EPA employees also have the authority to inspect the premises and records of persons involved in hazardous waste management. However, the various states are actively seeking authorization from the EPA to conduct part or all of the elements of a complete Resource Conservation and Recovery Act (RCRA) hazardous waste program, so inspections by federal employees will become less common in the future.

Inspections need not be announced in advance. For routine inspections, an inspector may call the contact person named in the notification form or in the permit application. This giving of a few day's notice is mainly to ensure that person(s) knowledgeable about the facility's waste management program and practices will be available. This advance notice allows the facility contact to arrange to have all key facility personnel on hand, and to get all required documents, plans and records in one place to expedite the inspection. However, federal law does not require advance notice, only that the inspector request access and present credentials, enter the establishment at reasonable times and that the inspection be commenced and completed with reasonable promptness. It must be noted that the regulations [40 CFR 265.55] require that, at all times, at least one employee (the emergency coordinator) familiar with all hazardous waste management activities of the facility be on the premises or on call. As a result, the excuse that no knowledgeable person is available to meet with the inspector is not a very good one for turning an inspector away. Further, it is a *prima facie* violation of the regulations.

Section 3007(a) of RCRA (PL 94-580), gives inspectors very broad inspection authority. State hazardous waste management statutes usually have similarly broad authority. Any person who "generates, stores, treats, transports, disposes of, or otherwise handles or has handled hazardous wastes shall, upon request . . . furnish information relating to such wastes and permit [the inspector] at all reasonable times to have access to, and copy all records relating to such wastes." Inspectors are authorized "(1) to enter at reasonable times any establishment or other place where hazardous wastes are or have been generated, stored, treated, disposed of, or transported from; and (2) to inspect and obtain samples from any person of any such wastes and samples of any containers or labeling for such wastes." A state need not have interim or final authorization from the EPA for designated employees of the state to have access for inspection or investigation purposes.

The inspector should introduce himself and willingly furnish his credentials on arriving at the manufacturing facility. At a minimum, the inspector should show an employee identification card from the state environmental agency. A business card is often provided, and in some states without interim or final authorization, the EPA has provided a one-page document entitled "compliance inspection credentials and designation" (Figure 8). In Indiana, inspectors are told not to sign liability waivers, confidentiality agreements or other preconditions on their access to the facility. Even if such agreements were signed, they would not be binding on the state regulatory authority. If the inspector will be shown trade secrets or confidential information (this should be unlikely), there are other methods of protecting such information.

The facility contact should examine the inspector's documentation and credentials before granting access to the facility and the records. It should be noted that the generator, by giving notification of hazardous waste activities and by (under certain circumstances) submitting an application for a hazardous waste permit, has entered a highly regulated area. The inspector will have little or no trouble obtaining a search warrant should access be denied. Refusing entry to an inspector will arouse suspicions and give reason for intensive scrutiny. If, for any

Under authority delegated to me by the Regional Administrator of the U. S.
Environmental Protection Agency Region V.

(Inspector)

whose signature appears below, is designated as an authorized representative of
the Environmental Protection Agency for the purpose of conducting inspections
pursuant to Section 3007(a) of the Resource Conservation and Recovery Act ("RCRA").

The inspector may: a) enter at reasonable times upon the premises where hazardous
wastes are or have been handled, generated, stored, treated, transported from or
disposed of; b) request and be furnished information relating to such wastes; and
c) inspect and obtain samples of any wastes and samples of any containers or
labeling for such wastes. These duties are to be performed in accordance with
the Cooperative Arrangement between EPA and the State of Indiana.

The inspector shall give to the owner, operator, or agent in charge a receipt
describing all samples obtained and if requested a portion retained. If any
analysis is made of such samples, a copy of the results of such analysis shall
be furnished promptly to the owner, operator, or agent in charge.

Section 3007(b) of RCRA and 40 CFR Part 2 define the Agency's policies
regarding protection of trade secrets and confidential information.

Date Issued:_____

Expiration Date_____

_____
(signature)
Designated Representative

_____
(signature)
Division Director
EPA Region V

Figure 8.   Compliance inspection credentials and designation.

reason, the inspector is refused entry or consent to the inspection is withdrawn during the inspection, the inspector must leave the premises.

If the manufacturing firm filed as a treatment, storage or disposal (TSD) facility, the inspector will bring a copy of the EPA forms 3510-1 and 3510-3 of the application for a hazardous waste permit (also known as "Part A") filed by the facility owner or operator. The inspector will use a special form (Appendix 5) to record the results of his observations. This form, the "RCRA Inspection Report," will document the inspector's findings in a "yes," "no" or "not inspected" fashion. However, the report includes a column for remarks, and the entire last page is devoted to a description of site activities observed at the time of the inspection. The inspector will have reviewed the firm's notification of hazardous waste activity (EPA form 8700-12), and any information relative to the facility on file at the state regulatory agency. The inspector will also be generally familiar with common industrial operations and processes, and general waste management practices.

The inspection itself has several purposes. Obviously the verification of the correctness and completeness of the notification form and permit application is one purpose. An inspection has enforcement purposes. i.e., to detect and document violations and discover imminent hazards and to support enforcement actions. A third, often unstated, purpose is to review and evaluate the overall waste management program and practices at the facility. The third evaluation often has some bearing on the overall scrutiny and frequency of inspection given the facility.

To determine the compliance status of the facility in question, the inspector must actually visit the areas where hazardous wastes are generated, accumulated, treated or stored. He will also have to sift through the mounds of "paperwork" associated with the hazardous waste management requirements. If at all possible, offer the inspector a tour of the manufacturing operations, in addition to that of the waste management areas. This will allow him to fit the waste management aspects of the facility into plant operations as a whole.

A routine inspection takes two to three hours to perform. When he was a state hazardous waste facility inspector, the author had a definite preference for the sequence of the inspection. The author's preference was first to sit down with the facility contact and any other interested parties to explain why the inspection is being performed and the statutory authority for the inspection; what the inspection will entail; and which documents will be reviewed. After this introduction, the inspection report will be completed with respect to those items readily ascertained by reviewing the paperwork. Table IX (Chapter 11) lists the documents that comprise the compliance paperwork. At this point the facility tour is in order, allowing the inspector to view the items and areas that must be seen to verify compliance (i.e., danger signs, condition of containers, or evidence of spills, leaks or explosions). After the tour, the inspection report is completed, and the facility contact will again call together any other interested parties for the conclusion. During the concluding remarks, the inspector will note the deficiencies observed and, if necessary, give the relevant regulatory citations for those deficiencies. This last session offers a unique opportunity to use the knowledge and experience of the inspector. By asking questions, other methods of doing things can be discussed as well as the actions, activities and equipment that will be necessary to remedy the deficiencies noted. However, inspectors are not consultants, nor will they recommend equipment or consultants. However, inspectors can be used as one source of information. For example, copies of statutes and regulations and lists of commercial hazardous waste management firms located in the state may be available from the state regulatory agency.

At the last session, the potential outcomes of the state regulatory agency's review of the inspector's report can be discussed. In most cases, a notice of violation (NOV) letter or compliance order (CO) will be issued. The inspector has limited input in the decision. Both letters are accompanied by a copy of the inspection report filled out by the inspector. A NOV letter will note the deficiencies and the required actions. These actions are to be taken within 30 days, and a written response must be sent to the state regulatory agency (and sometimes the EPA also) within 35 days detailing the actions taken. A CO is more serious, often accompanied by a fine and an administrative hearing. A CO requires the specified activities to be performed, and compliance to be achieved, within a specified time period. A facility may be reinspected to verify completion of activities outlined in the facility's response letter to a NOV or a CO. The topic of penalties and enforcement is covered in Chapter 22.

A few other items related to the topic of inspections need mentioning. If any samples are collected, the inspector should furnish a receipt. The facility representative has the right to request and receive duplicates ("split samples") of any samples taken. If any analysis is performed on the samples, a copy of the results is to be furnished to the facility. The completed inspection report and any correspondence (NOV, CO or other) relating to the inspection are available to the public. Claims of confidentiality can be made with respect to information entitled to protection under 18 USC 1905.

Chapter 22

LEGAL RESPONSIBILITIES AND LIABILITIES

John M. Kyle, III

    Barnes & Thornburg
    Indianapolis, Indiana

The subject of the legal responsibilities and liabilities attendant to handling hazardous wastes and hazardous substances is complex and constantly evolving, and properly is the subject of an entire book in itself. Consequently, fine points might be blurred and subtleties ignored in the discussion that follows. With this caveat, let us explore the major legal issues involved.

Previous chapters have discussed the statutory and regulatory requirements for handling hazardous waste pursuant to the Resource Conservation and Recovery Act (RCRA). However, RCRA and RCRA-authorized regulations are not the only sources of legal responsibilities applicable to handling hazardous waste. Other requirements may arise from state or federal common law, the Comprehensive Environmental Response, Compensation and Liability Act (Superfund), and state statutes and regulations.

It is beyond the scope of this chapter to analyze the wide variety of state requirements, which may differ from and be more stringent than RCRA requirements. A company doing business in any state must consult state statutes and regulations (and state common law; see below) to determine what additional requirements must be met.

This chapter will first analyze potential enforcement penalties for violating RCRA and RCRA regulations, and then discuss the requirements and liabilities under Superfund and common law. As can be seen from the discussion below, noncompliance can result in severe civil penalties and, in some cases, jail terms for responsible corporate officers.

RESOURCE CONSERVATION AND RECOVERY ACT

RCRA establishes a wide variety of standards of conduct applicable to generators, transporters, treaters, storers and disposers of hazardous wastes. Many of these requirements are "self-executing"—for example, compliance with transportation regulations is required without any further action by EPA. Other regulations, such as those for hazardous waste treatment, storage and disposal (TSD) facilities, are specifically applied to a particular facility through a U.S. Environmental Protection Agency (EPA) or state permit [1]. Compliance with such permits constitutes full compliance with RCRA Subtitle C regulations (but not with Section 7003 actions for imminent hazards, Superfund or common law), and erects a temporary shield from evolving standards under RCRA [1].

Civil Penalties

Section 3008 of RCRA (42 USC Sec. 6928) provides severe civil and criminal penalties for violations of self-executing standards and permits. If EPA determines that any person is violating "any requirement" of subtitle C (the regulatory heart of RCRA), it may issue a compliance order or commence a civil action against the alleged violator in federal district court for "appropriate relief," including injunctions and penalties of up to $25,000/day of violation. Any compliance order issued by EPA may suspend or revoke a permit, and shall specify (1) the nature of the violation; (2) a time for compliance; and (3) a penalty of up to $25,000/day of violation. No such order becomes final if the person subject to it requests a hearing within 30 days. After a hearing is held, EPA may either reinstate or modify its original order [42 USC § 6929(a), (b) and (c)].

Criminal Penalties

In addition to these civil penalties, Section 3008(d) establishes two categories of criminal penalties applicable to individuals and corporations. This section provides penalties for anyone who "knowingly":

1.   transports hazardous waste to a TSD facility that does not have a permit;
2.   transports, stores or disposes of hazardous waste without or contrary to a permit;

3. makes a false material statement in records required under RCRA; or
4. destroys, alters or conceals any records required under RCRA.

If convicted of points 1 or 2, the individual or corporation will be fined up to $50,000/day of violation, imprisoned up to two years or both. Those convicted of violating points 3 or 4 may be fined up to $25,000/day and imprisoned up to one year, or both. A second conviction under points 3 or 4 may be punished by the enhanced penalties applicable to points 1 or 2. As Quarles [1] states, little solace will be gathered from Congress' use of the word "knowingly," since it probably means only that a defendant must be aware of the nature of his conduct and the attendant circumstances. For example, the fact that a defendant did not know that he handled a "RCRA-hazardous" waste will undoubtedly be irrelevant.

Section 3008(e) creates a second category of criminal penalties for more egregious conduct. Conviction for the crime of "knowing endangerment" may result to anyone

1. who knowingly (1) transports hazardous waste to a facility without a permit; (2) treats, stores or disposes of hazardous waste without or contrary to a permit; or (3) having applied for a permit, fails to include material information in such an application, or fails to comply with interim status standards;
2. who knows at the time that "he thereby places another in imminent danger of death or serious bodily injury;" and
3. whose conduct manifests "an unjustified and inexcusable disregard for human life" or "extreme indifference for human life."

Violators are subject to fines of up to $250,000 imprisonment up to two years or both. Any person convicted of "extreme indifference for human life" may be imprisoned up to five years. An organization convicted of knowing endangerment may be fined up to $1 million. Although these provisions are obviously geared to extremely egregious conduct, they represent the most severe penalties associated with violation of any federal environmental statute.

EPA "Phase One" Enforcement Policy

As discussed in Chapter 1, Congress recognized that EPA could not develop final standards for TSD facilities and issue permits incorporating these standards quickly. Therefore, RCRA provides that anyone who (1) notified EPA by August 18, 1980, of hazardous wastes activity; (2) owned or operated a TSD facility in existence on November 19, 1980; and (3) submitted Part A of a TSD facility permit application by November 19, 1980, was granted "interim status" and allowed to continue operating until Part B of this application was requested, submitted, evaluated and acted on. Several interim status standards and certain self-executing standards (e.g., standards for generators and transportators) apply during "Phase One."

On July 7, 1981, EPA established a three-tiered enforcement policy for Phase One [2]. EPA has not yet established a similar enforcement policy for Phase Two. Under the Phase One policy, EPA divided violations into three categories based on the immediacy of harm or threat of harm to the public or environment.

Class One

Class one violations are violations that "pose direct and immediate harm or threats of harm to public health or the environment" and include:

1. violation of interim status requirements that result in a discharge or imminent threat of discharge to the environment;
2. failure by generators or transporters to use the manifest system;
3. shipment by a generator to a facility with neither interim status nor a permit;
4. delivery by a transporter to a facility not designated by the generator on the manifest;
5. requirements concerning condition of containers;
6. failure to comply with immediate action requirements and discharge cleanup requirements when hazardous waste is discharged during transportation;
7. failure to comply with special requirements for ignitable, reactive or incompatible wastes; and
8. substantial noncompliance with security requirements.

Class one violations will be dealt with through a Section 7003 imminent hazard or a Section 3008 judicial action in federal district court, or a Section 3008 EPA-issued compliance order.

Class Two

Class two violations involve noncompliance with specific statutory requirements not requiring specific implementing regulations, and include:

1. failure to notify EPA of hazardous waste activity under Section 3010;
2. failure to comply with Section 3005 permit requirements; and
3. failure to obtain interim status.

These violations will be addressed by a Section 3008 judicial action, a Section 3008 EPA-issued compliance order, or an "interim status compliance letter" describing necessary remedial actions, depending on the seriousness of the violation.

Class Three

Class three violations involve minor "procedural or reporting violations which, in themselves, do not pose direct short-term threats to the public health or environment." These include:

1. reporting requirements such as annual reports;
2. personnel training requirements;
3. inspection schedule requirements;
4. labeling, marking, and placarding requirements;
5. failure to consult with local authorities;
6. identification number requirements;
7. failure by a generator to furnish a sufficient number of copies of a manifest.

These violations will normally be addressed outside the formal administrative process by a warning letter stating the areas of noncompliance, necessary remedial measures and that continued noncompliance might result in a Section 3008 order or other enforcement action.

A contemporaneous violation of both class one and class two will be dealt with simultaneously through a Section 7003 or 3008 judicial action or an administrative order. If a person violates class three requirements in addition to either class one or class two, EPA will issue a contemporaneous warning letter regarding the class three violation in addition to other more formal administrative action regarding class one or class two violations.

SUPERFUND

As stated above, RCRA is not the only source of duties and liabilities associated with handling hazardous substances. One of RCRA's major shortcomings was that it principally governed activities after the effective date of RCRA or RCRA regulations; with the exception of a Section 7003 lawsuit to address imminent hazards, RCRA did not address the problems of inactive sites or past disposal practices. (Section 7003 of RCRA [42 USC 6973] provides that EPA may sue to obtain appropriate relief for "imminent and substantial" dangers to public health or the environment. This section has been subjected to varying judicial interpretations, discussion of which is beyond the scope of this chapter.) Moreover, RCRA did not define a company's liabilities for a release of hazardous substances into the environment. To remedy such problems, Congress passed Superfund in late 1980.

The main thrust of Superfund was to create a $1.6 billion fund to clean up inactive sites posing a threat to the public health or environment. However, Superfund did much more. In addition to Superfund's revenue-creating aspects, it also created certain regulatory requirements, filling certain gaps in RCRA's prospective system [3].

First, Section 103(c) [42 USC § 9603(c)], established reporting requirements for hazardous waste sites not covered by RCRA. Within 180 days of December 11, 1980, past and present owners or operators of, or any person who accepted hazardous waste for transportation to, a facility where hazardous substances (the definition of which is much broader than that of hazardous wastes) "are or have been stored, treated, or disposed of, shall, unless such facility has a permit" or interim status under RCRA, notify EPA of the existence of such facility and specify "the amount and type of any hazardous substances to be found there, and any known, suspected, or likely release of such substances from the facility." Failure to notify could result in a $10,000 fine, or imprisonment for one year, or both. EPA is also authorized to adopt regulations regarding the location of such facilities and the hazardous substances contained there, and to specify records that must be maintained by anyone required to notify under this section. It is unlawful for anyone to destroy or otherwise render unavailable any records required to be kept under these regulations for a period of 50 years unless a waiver is obtained from EPA.

Sections 103(a) and (b) [42 U.S.C. §§ 9603(a) and (b)] provide that anyone in charge of a vessel or onshore or offshore facility must immediately notify the National Response Center if hazardous substances are released into the environment from such vessel or facility. "Release" and "environment" are *very* broadly defined to cover nearly every type of spill, discharge, leaching or disposal of hazardous waste into the air, land or water. Notification does not need to occur unless there is a release of a "reportable quantity," originally defined as one pound, and since amended to provide variable quantities for a variety of substances. Once again, failure to report such a release can result in a fine of $10,000 or imprisonment for up to one year, or both.

Although Superfund authorizes the President to respond to any such "release" or threat of release by spending a portion of the $1.6 billion fund, the fund cannot begin to pay for cleaning up all such sites. Even though the statute allows EPA or the President to recover response costs from any "responsible party" [42 USC § 9607(a)], Superfund also allows the President, if there is an imminent and substantial danger to public health or environment arising from a release or threatened release of hazardous substances from a facility, to require the U.S. Attorney General to file suit in federal court to obtain "such relief as the public interest . . . may require" [42 U.S.C. § 9606(a)]. In addition, the President may issue an order "as may be necessary to protect the public health or the environment" [42 USC § 9606(a)]. Anyone who fails to comply with such an order may be fined $5000/day of noncompliance. Thus, Superfund authorizes direct action against responsible parties to force cleanup of sites releasing or threatening to release hazardous substances into the environment.

Superfund attempts to define a company's liability for (1) state or federal remedial action costs "not inconsistent with the national contingency plan" (NCP); (2) necessary response costs incurred by "any other person consistent with" NCP; and (3) damages to natural resources [42 USC Sec. 9607(a)]. The act also required EPA to expand the NCP (originally required under the Clean Water Act and formerly applicable to spills of oil or hazardous substances) to cover "releases" of hazardous substances into the "environment." This expanded plan will govern responses to such releases.

Past and present owners or operators of a vessel or facility; any person who arranged for disposal or treatment of hazardous substances at or arranged with a transporter for transport of hazardous substances to such a facility owned or operated by another entity; and any person who accepts or accepted hazardous substances for transport to such a facility, from which there is a release or threatened release, which causes the incurrence of response costs, shall be liable for (1) all cleanup costs incurred by the United States or the state; (2) any other necessary response costs incurred by any other person; and (3) damages to natural resources. Although this section of Superfund defining liability only expressly applies to defray the costs set out in the text, many, including the U.S. Department of Justice and EPA, feel it also defines liability in abatement actions brought under Section 106.

Thus, Superfund does much more than provide for cleanup of sites from which a release is or may occur—it also seeks to define a company's liability for such a release. This liability provision requires further discussion.

It is generally accepted that Superfund creates strict liability for those who handle hazardous substances. No amount of care will insulate a person handling hazardous substances from liability. Thus, Superfund accomplishes what RCRA failed to address; a person can no longer contract away responsibility for a release into the environment. If a person sends wastes to a landfill, for example, and that landfill later releases or threatens to release hazardous substances into the environment, the original generator of waste may be held liable for at least a proportionate share of the costs of preventing or cleaning up that release.

The federal government contends that Superfund also creates joint and several liability; this means that if two or more persons contribute waste to a site, any one of those persons may be held liable for the entire costs of cleaning up the site. This issue is hotly contested. Earlier drafts of Superfund expressly provided that liability would be strict, as well as joint and several. However, these provisions were deleted from the statute so that the bill would be able to pass Congress. Whether federal courts can fill in this gap in the statute and still create federal joint and several liability is discussed below.

COMMON LAW

The federal statutes discussed above were not written in a void, but rather against the preexisting background of common law, i.e., not statutes or regulations, but laws made by judges. The question addressed in this section is whether other obligations or liabilities attach to handling hazardous materials as a result of common law. There are two potential sources of additional liabilities: federal common law and state common law.

Federal Common Law

It must be emphasized that federal common law is limited and applies only in the absence of an applicable act of Congress. Recent decisions of the U.S. Supreme Court hold that when Congress enacts a comprehensive environmental statute containing detailed standards of conduct, authorizing comprehensive administrative regulations supervised by an expert agency and providing elaborate provisions for enforcement of those standards, federal courts are not free to alter the terms of the statute by developing new standards of conduct or engrafting nonstatutory remedies onto the statute [4]. In such an event, federal statutes preempt—or prevent federal judges from developing further—federal common law. Taken together, RCRA and Superfund certainly establish a comprehensive Congressional scheme addressed to nearly every phase of hazardous waste management. Therefore, there is a strong argument that federal judges will not be able to fill in certain gaps in these statutes by recognizing joint and several liability or developing a right of contribution among multiple contributors to a site since Congress said all it had to say on the subject. On the other hand, there is an argument, at least insofar as Superfund is concerned, that Superfund is not a comprehensive regulatory statute, but, as compared to RCRA, and the Clean Water and Clean Air Acts, is rather simple and straightforward. Therefore, the argument runs, Congress did not occupy the entire field and judges have the authority to develop common law and recognize joint and several liability or contribution. Moreover, there are strong indications in Superfund's legislative history that sections explicitly providing joint and several liability and contribution were deleted from the statute with the express, congressional understanding that courts would be free to develop these theories as appropriate on a case by case basis.

The answer to whether federal judges have continuing authority to "make law" in this area depends on how broad the questions addressed by Superfund are, which in turn defines the scope of preemption of common law [4-7]. To date, this question has not been resolved by the courts, and it is impossible to predict the result. At the very least, it is clear that federal judges' law-making authority will be limited to simply filling gaps in the statutes, such as rights of contribution and joint and several liability, and will not be allowed to recognize completely nonstatutory federal common law causes of action such as a federal cause of action in nuisance.

State Common Law

It is clear from recent Supreme Court decisions that comprehensive federal environmental statutes do not preempt state common law. State common law is not limited, as is federal common law, and may be used not only to fill gaps in statutory schemes, but also to recognize wholly separate and distinct causes of action. There is a potential argument that, just as federal statutes preempt federal common law, state statutes and regulations may preempt state common law; however, most state courts that have addressed this issue have concluded that, in the absence of strong state legislative intent in favor of such preemption, state common law remains.

As mentioned, state common law will not be limited to filling in gaps, but may be used to develop entirely new and different nonstatutory causes of action. Several common law theories apply to handling hazardous waste. Examples include the law of nuisance, strict liability for ultrahazardous activities, trespass and negligence. It is beyond the scope of this chapter to discuss fully the elements of these causes of action. However, very briefly, a nuisance encompasses any activity or situation that is injurious to health or offensive to the senses and that interferes with the comfortable enjoyment of life and property. A landfill that leaches contaminants into groundwater, thereby polluting neighboring wells or a public body of water, would certainly be a nuisance. Most states hold that even a lawfully operated business in compliance with all applicable laws and regulations may still constitute a nuisance. Therefore, compliance with statutes and regulations such as RCRA and Superfund would not be a defense to a nuisance action.

The doctrine of strict liability for ultrahazardous activities essentially provides that one who carries on an abnormally dangerous activity that results in harm to another will be held liable for such harm, despite the exercise of utmost care and precautions. Existence of this strict liability tort depends on whether a given activity constitutes an "ultrahazardous activity." In the past, activities such as blasting and mining operations have been held to constitute such an activity. More recently, some state courts have held that handling hazardous waste constitutes an ultrahazardous activity resulting in strict liability [8]. However, it should also be noted that other states have held just the opposite [9]. Most states have not addressed the issue at all. The law of each state must be reviewed to determine whether this far-reaching liability attaches to handling hazardous substances.

Unlike strict liability, to be held liable under a negligence theory a company or individual must be "at fault" or have failed to exercise a "reasonable standard of care" in handling hazardous substances. For example, if a generator of hazardous waste fails to follow any RCRA standard, such as those relating to storage or containerization of wastes, and if such a failure causes damage to another party, that party could sue on a negligence theory, claiming the defendant failed to comply with a reasonable standard of careful conduct.

Finally, trespass is simply an unauthorized entrance onto the land of another, which could occur if hazardous substances were spilled from a truck or leached from a landfill onto another's property.

In all of these common law theories, a plaintiff must overcome a substantial hurdle referred to in the law as "proximate cause." Essentially, proximate cause means that defendant's activity must be "reasonably forseeable" and the direct and relatively immediate cause of plaintiff's injury; there cannot be intervening or superseding activities of others that "break the chain of causation" and become the "major," "superseding" or "more important" cause of plaintiff's injuries. The confused doctrine can be best explained with an example. If a generator contracts with a transporter to haul hazardous waste to a given disposal site, and, rather than transport the waste to the identified disposal site, the transporter instead dumps the waste along the road, thereby injuring a plaintiff, the defendant generator would argue that the transporter's intervening act was the proximate cause of plaintiff's injury and that it was not reasonably forseeable that the transporter would illegally dump the waste. On the other hand, if the transporter took the waste to the identified landfill and the fill later leached and caused damage to someone, proximate cause may exist because there would be no dramatic, intervening cause and such damage would be reasonably forseeable. The lack of proximate cause would be a proper defense to the common law causes of action discussed above, and exonerate the defendant generator from liability. The doctrine varies substantially from state to state, and it is impossible to discuss the many permutations and variations on this theme in the scope of this chapter.

CONCLUSION

As can be seen, there is a very good reason to comply with the requirements of the law of hazardous substances—noncompliance can hurt. The costs of developing and implementing a company-wide compliance program may seem infinitesimal when compared to the penalties associated with noncompliance, the bad publicity that may ensue, and the fact that, once caught, such a program will be required anyway. Corporate planners must be aware of the fact that compliance with statutory and regulatory requirements may not be enough—additional burdens may be imposed through common law. Therefore, working knowledge of state common law will help companies further define and refine their duties and liabilities in this area.

REFERENCES

1. Quarles, J. *Federal Regulation of Hazardous Waste: A Guide to RCRA* (Environmental Law Institute, 1982), p. 149.
2. EPA Enforcement Memorandum, July 7, 1981.
3. Dore, M. "The Standard of Civil Liability for Hazardous Waste Disposal Activity: Some Quirks of Superfund," *Notre Dame Lawyer* 57:260,268 (1981).
4. *Middlesex County* v. *National Seaclammers,* 453 U.S. 1 (1981).
5. *Milwaukee* v. *Illinois,* 451 U.S. 304 (1981).
6. *In Re Oswego Barge,* 664 F.2d 327 (2nd Cir. 1981).
7. *Illinois* v. *Outboard Marine,* 680 F.2d 473 (7th Cir. 1982).
8. *State* v. *Ventron Corp.,* 440 A.2d 455 (New Jersey 1981).
9. *Uehl* v. *Petro Processors,* 364 So. 2d 604 (Louisiana 1978).

Chapter 23

FINANCIAL ASSURANCE: REQUIREMENTS AND OPTIONS FOR HAZARDOUS WASTE MANAGEMENT FACILITIES

John Lindenschmidt

Marsh & McClennon
Indianapolis, Indiana

Attempting compliance with the financial aspects of the U.S. Environmental Protection Agency (EPA) regulations (40 CFR 265, Subpart H) can generate enough confusion to frustrate even the best risk manager. Providing your company with financial assurance as mandated by state and federal hazardous waste management (HWM) regulations is a difficult endeavor. "Financial assurance" will be used in this chapter to include money for closure as well as for liability protection. This chapter will explain the federal requirements in this area, and the options available to meet these requirements. In addition, the efforts necessary to move toward the desirable goal of "prudent risk management" will be outlined.

Prudent risk management can be thought of as guarding company assets by providing the most financially sound and cost-effective insurance mechanism(s) for exposure to loss. Prudent risk management must also be legal, and meet all statutory and regulatory requirements.

It is important to understand that, as with other aspects of the Resource Conservation and Recover Act (RCRA), individual states may have financial requirements different from or reaching beyond those of EPA. Comprehension of any differences between state and federal regulations is essential. This has too often been an oversight of companies focusing solely on meeting federal requirements, oblivious to what is happening on the home front.

As explained in Section 1, determination of the firm's regulatory category with respect to HWM activities is critical to compliance. Manufacturing firms that are generators who accumulate hazardous wastes under 90 days do not fall under the Subpart H financial requirements. Other categories are also exempt from these requirements, as the only category subject to the financial requirements is that of treatment, storage or disposal (TSD) facility. Transporters of hazardous wastes fall under U.S. Department of Transportation (DOT) regulations regarding liability coverage.

Manufacturing firms with onsite hazardous waste storage facilities (storage in containers or storage in tanks) are required to be financially responsible for the costs of closing the HWM facility. In addition, the firm is to be responsible for potential liabilities to third parties associated with the ownership/operation of such facilities.

As alluded to above, there are two aspects to such a firm's financial responsibilities with respect to their onsite hazardous waste management facilities. The first aspect is assurance of sufficient funds to properly close the storage facility in accordance with the closure plan. This aspect is required regardless of the firm's intentions regarding closure of the plant or the hazardous waste facility. Most manufacturers intend to keep their plants (and storage facilities) open well into the twenty-first century.

The second aspect of the firm's financial responsibilities is the demonstration of responsibility for any claims made by third parties to compensate for damages resulting from the operations of the HWM facility. Normally, this entails maintaining a liability insurance policy with the proper provisions and levels of coverage. For storage facilities, responsibility would need to be demonstrated only for sudden and accidental occurrences (fires, explosions, spills or leaks) resulting from facility operations.

CLOSURE GUARANTEES

As of this writing, the current federal requirements dealing with financial responsibility for closure were promulgated as a "revised interim final rule" on April 7, 1982, in the *Federal Register* (47 FR 15032). This promulgation revised Subpart H—Financial Requirements, of 40 CFR 264 and 265. For facilities under interim status, only the Part 265 standards apply. The mechanisms now allowed for assurance of closure costs include:

1. closure trust fund;
2. surety bond guaranteeing payment into a trust fund;
3. letters of credit,
4. financial test and corporate guarantee,
5. closure insurance policy, or
6. combinations of options 1, 2, 3 and 5.

It is important to realize that the market for these options for HWM facilities is evolving. Options such as surety bonds, letters of credit, and insurance policies will be difficult to obtain, except for major corporations with proven financial strength.

The financial requirements for postclosure care will not be discussed in this chapter, as they pertain only to disposal facilities and facilities where hazardous wastes remain after closure (landfills, surface impoundments and land treatment facilities). Such requirements were briefly discussed in Chapter 18.

LIABILITY COVERAGE

Owners or operators of TSD facilities, in addition to closure guarantees, are required to have sudden and accidental liability coverage for bodily injury and property damage to third parties resulting from facility operations. The current federal requirements on this aspect of financial responsibility were promulgated as a "revised interim final rule" on April 16, 1982, in the *Federal Register* (47 FR 16554). This amendment revised Subpart H—Financial Requirements, of 40 CFR 264 and 265. For facilities under interim status, only the Part 265 standards apply. The mechanisms allowed for demonstration of liability coverage are:

1. insurance policy,
2. financial test (self-insurance), or
3. combination of options 1 and 2.

Owners or operators of hazardous waste TSD facilities are required to submit evidence of liability coverage for sudden and accidental occurrences in minimum amounts of $1 million per occurrence, $2 million annual aggregate (exclusive of legal defense costs). This submission may be in the form of a certificate of insurance (if an insurance policy is used) or statements from the firm's chief financial officer and from an independent certified public accountant (if the financial test is used). Such evidence of liability coverage is to be submitted to EPA in states without interim authorization or financial responsibility regulations. Otherwise, evidence of liability coverage is to be submitted to the state hazardous waste management agency. A telephone call or letter of inquiry to the state regulatory agency will confirm the financial responsibility requirements of the state in which the facility is located.

FINANCIAL ASSURANCE FOR NONSUDDEN/GRADUAL INCIDENTS

It is important to understand that there is a subclassification of TSD facilities whose owner or operator is required to demonstrate additional financial assurances. This subclassification encompasses TSD facilities that have land disposal facilities, land treatment facilities or surface impoundments where wastes remain after closure.

Facilities that fall into this subclassification must have, in addition to the closure/postclosure and sudden and accidental assurances, proof of liability coverage for nonsudden and gradual occurrences. The most common example of a nonsudden and gradual occurrence is the contamination of down-gradient drinking water wells from offsite migration of hazardous wastes through the subsurface.

The regulations (40 CFR 265, Subpart H) require, at a minimum, that owners or operators of such facilities provide coverage in the amounts of $3 million per occurrence with a $6 million annual aggregate. As with sudden and accidental liability coverage, the nonsudden liability assurances can be provided through an insurance policy typically called an environmental impairment liability (EIL) policy, or by using the financial test (self-insurance) or by some combination of the two.

The requirements for nonsudden liability coverage are being phased in. Owner/operators with annual sales or revenues of $10 million or more will be required to submit evidence of nonsudden coverage by January 16, 1983. Those with annual sales or revenues of $5–10 million will be required to submit such evidence by January 16, 1984. All other TSD facilities requiring nonsudden liability coverage must submit evidence of it by January 16, 1985.

The financial test may be an attractive option. Weighing the pros and cons of whether to use a financial test and basically self-insure or to transfer the risk to an EIL policy is a decision that deserves considerable thought. Use of the financial test eliminates any fee or premium. A transfer of risk to an EIL policy is like any other insurance policy, such as homeowner's or auto, in that it protects assets from the catastrophic or large-dollar-loss claims.

Considerations for determining which mechanism to use should center around three basic questions:

1. What is the potential for loss from past, present and future waste activities?
2. What is the maximum foreseeable loss that could result from a nonsudden pollution incident (although difficult to determine)?
3. Is the company willing to accept or in a financial position to pay for this foreseeable loss?

The transfer of risk for nonsudden and gradual occurrences (from hazardous waste facilities and activities) through an EIL policy may be desirable to manufacturing firms not otherwise required to maintain such insurance. Circumstances that may behoove a firm to seek such a transfer of risk include:

1. Past use of onsite waste management facilities (landfills, surface impoundments) that were properly closed prior to the effective date of RCRA;
2. Past use of now-abandoned offsite facilities for the disposal of industrial wastes that would now be classified as hazardous; and
3. improper past waste management practices (spills, leaks, burning, dumping, pits, ponds or lagoons) in areas of existing plant property where the geology is inadequate to slow or restrict the subsurface movement of hazardous wastes or constituents.

If an EIL policy is required or desired, it is important to comparison-shop. A combination of self insurance and an EIL may be desirable. In essence, this combination would be similar to establishing a deductible for the insurance policy, and is a good way to reduce premiums.

Shopping for an EIL policy is fairly involved. Availability of insurance carriers who will contemplate providing EIL coverage has greatly expanded from only four in early 1982 to 13 at last count. The market is expected to further expand as the reluctant companies jump into the market after the trail blazers have worked out the bugs in the policies and established a loss history record. The developing competitive nature of the marketplace has shown improvements in the broadening of coverages and more aggressive pricing. This is certainly good news for those needing or wanting such coverage.

Comparison quotations for EIL coverage typically involve an environmental risk assessment (ERA) survey. The ERA survey is an evaluation by an outside consultant, identifying the extent of exposure and basically rating the risk (low, medium and high) to provide an underwriter with enough information to quote coverage.

Insurance brokers/agents are in a favorable position to assist companies in the best placement of coverage. Major brokers/agents will have a technical service staff which will be capable of providing the ERA to be used in marketing nonsudden coverage. The broker's technical service, being independent of the insurance company, can provide waste management consulting to improve the company's waste management program before deriving and marketing the ERA survey. After interpreting the ERA, the broker's marketing staff will be in a position to assist in determining policy limits, sizes of deductibles and types of policies best suited to the company.

ERA SURVEY

To provide assistance in obtaining the best EIL quotation, the following will be the points of major emphasis to the engineer performing the assessment and to the underwriters providing the quotations.

Two major categories addressed by underwriters are the administrative programs in place to address the waste activities, and the extent of waste activities, past and present. Administratively, strong emphasis is placed on the attitude taken by the company toward controlling waste activities. This is exemplified by such things as:

1. corporate policy statement addressing the intent of management to control the situation and the establishment of a line of accountability to follow through with management's intentions;
2. establishment of an environmental affairs manager to coordinate activities on a corporate level;
3. for multiple locations, an individual assigned to coordinate waste activities at the separate plants; and
4. corporate and/or local loss control programs specifically addressing waste activities.

Evaluation of waste activities place emphasis on:

- compliance with local, state and federal regulations;
- degree of "hazard" of wastes;

- quantities and description of wastes generated;
- proximity of the TSD facility to drinking water supplies;
- geology of facility location; and
- in-depth description of past activities.

The third-party ERA is conducted to determine:

1. the likelihood of a lawsuit for injury to persons (not including employees) or property (not belonging to the potential insured) arising out of the present or past leakage or accumulative emissions from its facilities (normally graded on a scale described as low, moderate and high);
2. a reasonable deductible based on an expected level of environmental impairment liability; and
3. a reasonable limit of coverage based on degree of environmental risk and assessment of liability due to the occurrence of a "worst-case" incident.

For multiple locations it is desirable to seek a corporate policy to cover all the waste activities of every named location. This is beneficial in that it provides broader coverage and is usually more attractive to an underwriter when considering an overall package policy instead of site-specific coverage.

However, it may be determined by the ERA survey that one or more sites are of such high risk that trying to fold the sites into one policy would disproportionately affect the overall pricing of the company's EIL policy. In such a situation it would then be suggested to investigate self-insuring the "sore thumb" locations and bring the remainder of locations under one comprehensive policy.

POLLUTION LIABILITY POLICIES

In reviewing a pollution liability policy, it is necessary to be concerned with the definition of a pollution incident within the policy. For example, one definition states a pollution incident as:

> an emission, a discharge, release or escape of any solid, liquid, gas, gaseous or thermo contaminates, emissions or pollutants directly from the insured site into or upon land, the atmosphere, or any water course or body of water provided that such emission, discharge, release or escape results in an environmental damage.

The policy definition of a pollution incident differs from one policy to another. The definition of a pollution incident is the basis for the policy and should be reviewed with the company's activities in mind. The policy definition should be reviewed with the broker or underwriter to ensure that the definition and the coverage provided by such a definition is thoroughly understood.

All EIL policies are written on a claims-made basis as opposed to an occurrence basis. This is interpreted to mean that the policy is intended to cover pollution claims initiated during the policy period, which is typically one year. Defense costs are included in the policy limits in many of the forms being offered and there is a narrowing of coverage where defense costs are within the limits of the policy. The obligation to defend is not always as clear in policies that use language of indemnification as opposed to paying on behalf of their insured. For policies that include defense costs within the limits of the policy, it may legitimately be feared that a substantial portion of the policy limits would be "eaten up" by defense costs. Considering the possibility of "nuisance claims" and the potential for long, drawn-out court proceedings, consideration should be given to comparing policies that grant supplemental defense costs normally found in the comprehensive general liability (CGL) policy. The federal minimum coverage requirements are exclusive of legal defense costs.

Another area where there can be substantial differences among the pollution liability insurance forms is the granting of coverage for cleanup costs. The primary purpose of pollution coverage is to respond to third-party injuries, whether they be bodily injury or property damage. However, there will be environmental pollution incidents that require an insured to clean up third-party premises, and each of the forms now being written grant that coverage. However, a question arises as to what will take place when an environmental incident on the insured's site causes no damage outside the insured's property line. In some of the newly written or revised policy forms, language is to the effect that the insurers may exercise an option that calls for reimbursement of cleanup costs at the insured's site. However, this is only an option reserved by the insurer and is not a guarantee that insurance money will be available for onsite cleanup.

As with the other exclusions found in any pollution liability policy, the exclusion of onsite cleanup can be "bought back." This simply means that, for a price, the cost of onsite cleanup or other typical exclusions can be made a part of the policy coverage. This negotiation process is best handled by the insured's broker.

In reviewing the policy forms, it is important to remember that certain forms contain a retroactive date. This means that the coverage on these claims-made forms will go back to, but not beyond a particular date. Actually, this is a narrowing of coverage, as opposed to those forms that contain no retroactive date with commencement of coverage for pollution incidents which are discovered and first reported during the term of the particular claims-made policy. Because of the claims-made nature of the policies, it is essential that it contain a right to a discovery period to report losses in the event an insured changes insurers. Most forms currently offered are granting some discovery period, but the wording should be carefully examined to both check the length of time for such a discovery period and to analyze the conditions under which the extension is granted. Another point that should be reviewed in each policy is the definition regarding what constitutes a claim, i.e., written notice. It is important that the definition of a claim is clear and concise within the policy form purchased.

As an overview, the company has a number of various serious considerations with respect to the firm's need for pollution liability insurance. Initially, the question is whether or not the firm has such a liability. If it does, then the question is whether or not the risk manager should permit the CGL policy to respond for sudden and accidental incidents and purchase only pollution coverage on a separate policy for gradual pollution. This risk manager must consider if the coverage is mandated, whether by federal or state governments. Consideration must also be given to the various states in which a firm operates, if it is involved either in generation, transportation or TSD of hazardous wastes. The liability, if present, will exist regardless of any governmental regulations mandating insurance. The question of pollution insurance is similar to the question of insurance in any other avenue of risk transference. The corporate assets are to be protected, and a means of protecting those assets is one that the risk manager and the firm's management must deal with on the very practical basis of cost. The entire subject of environmental impairment liability insurance is in a state of flux and will continue in this mode for several years. The federal government has finally decided what its role should be in the area of mandating financial responsibility for those involved with hazardous wastes, but many states must now go through the same exercise. The policy forms are changing, the excess markets are seriously considering becoming involved, and there is every indication that the entire insurance industry—from the primary placement up through the excess layers—will eventually be ready and willing to accept pollution liability much the same as they would accept any other form of insurable risks. Whether the insurance is mandated by federal regulatory bodies or not, it certainly behooves any company that deals to any sufficient degree in hazardous waste activities to evaluate the extent of pollution exposure, and attempt to achieve prudent risk management.

Chapter 24

SELECTING A CONSULTANT

Bruce H. Palin
Engineering Section
Division of Land Pollution Control
Indiana State Board of Health
Indianapolis, Indiana

The advent of hazardous waste regulations has been the result of a natural progression of environmental concerns over air, water and land pollution. With the development of stricter controls over each of these areas, there have evolved the corresponding "experts" in the consulting field to assist industries and municipalities in responding to overwhelming volumes of regulations. Their services have almost become a necessity due to the complexities of the laws and the inability of some firms to maintain their own experts. Unfortunately, the environmental area has not been immune from those looking to capitalize on a new market where demand exceeds supply.

How does a manufacturing firm that generates hazardous waste locate a consulting firm or environmental engineer that can address a specific problem outside the expertise of in-house waste management personnel? The best answer is to shop around. If you were going to have the engine in your car overhauled, you would not take it to the first garage listed in the Yellow Pages. You would do some checking to try and locate a competent mechanic with experience. Granted, the extra time required to locate a good consultant may be an inconvenience, but it will pay off in the long run.

What does one look for when considering which consultant will be retained to address hazardous waste problems? First, outward appearances and impressive, colorful brochures do not guarantee competence. One must dig deeper to truly flush out an individual's or company's ability. There are a few superficial signs, however, to look for when interviewing. If their business card lists their areas of expertise and "hazardous waste" is penciled in under "wastewater treatment," scratch them from your list. Although somewhat exaggerated, this is a real example of what has resulted as federal funds for wastewater treatment have decreased and the emphasis on hazardous waste management has increased. Consultants have expanded their services to follow the market, and some have done it more successfully than others.

You may also note by the business card that the individual with which you are talking has the title of "environmental engineer." You should not jump to the obvious conclusion that this person has a degree in engineering, environmental or otherwise. Firms and companies have been known to hire someone from a regulatory agency with experience in hazardous waste and a scholastic background in public health and call him an environmental engineer. In some cases, the experience has been a better teacher; but it depends on the individual. At any rate, you should inquire into the individual's background and evaluate his ability based on his experiences as well as his education.

A good way to assess the type of work a consultant does is to ask for a list of their previous clients or projects and do some investigation into how well they performed on previous jobs. If the consultant suggests that as a first step he wants to conduct a "study" of your current waste production and management practices, ask to see similar studies they have conducted for other companies. Do not be surprised if his response in the negative contains words such as "proprietary" and "confidential." In fact, if he does not respond this way, you may want to be suspicious. If you should, by chance, be able to view one of their previous studies and it seems to be a standard, computer-generated form, with the details filled in by typewriter, go to the next name on your list. These fill-in-the-blank reports are usually a 500-page answer to a 10-page problem and have been used in the past by consultants to impress clients with the amount of information they receive for their money. The need to study a situation should not be minimized. Indeed, a considerable amount of time should be spent by the consultant familiarizing himself with the plant and talking to the people who operate the facility on a day-to-day basis, but you do not need a lengthy report to tell you what is already obvious or to explore options that are not practical.

Consultants are not necessarily free agents; some of them are connected with private haulers and commercial hazardous waste treatment, storage or disposal (TSD) facilities. This is a good thing to know if it turns out some of your waste must go offsite for handling. If this is the proposal, it would serve you well to check into the ability of the offsite facility to process your waste, even to the point of visiting the facility yourself and taking a tour. You do not have to be a trained inspector to determine whether a facility has a sloppy operation or not. Ask to see the drum storage area, as this is the area that is most often neglected and allowed to deteriorate. If they do not handle wastes in drums, they should score a few more points on your evaluation. If it is a treatment facility, ask the representative of the facility to walk you through the process your waste would follow, noting how the various by-products are handled. If it is a disposal facility, ask to see how they record the incoming waste and keep track of where various wastes are located within the disposal site. A more extensive discussion on this topic is found in Chapter 18.

Getting to know the state regulatory agency responsible for implementing the federal hazardous waste regulations can be a real asset. Their staff has worked with a variety of consultants on hazardous waste projects and have a great deal of first-hand knowledge on how well various firms perform. Do not expect, however, to get a thumbs up or down on a particular firm, as the representatives of state agencies are not in a position to endorse one company over another. They do, however, deal in facts, and if you ask the right questions, you will probably receive some indication as to a firm's track record. You first want to find out whether the agency is familiar with the consultant's work. Have they submitted plans or proposals for approval; if so, were they approved? If not, why not? Have any of the consultant's clients ended up in litigation? If so, what was the background leading to the litigation? Regulatory people will usually not discuss much about a pending legal action, but closed cases are a matter of public record. Depending on the type of rapport you have established with the regulatory agency staff, you may obtain some useful information on a prospective firm.

If you have wastes, hazardous or not, that are going offsite for treatment or disposal, the regulatory agency may be of assistance in helping you evaluate the performance of the receiving facility. You may want to arrange a visit to the agency office to review the file on the subject facility. The file will contain such information as the facility permit with operational conditions, inspection reports, violation letters, enforcement actions and agreed orders, if applicable. While at the agency office you should talk with the inspector responsible for your area about other facilities which could handle your waste. You may find out that your consultant has lined you up with a facility with which he is associated but that a much closer facility exists that could handle your material with a reduced transportation cost. The agency, of course, is a useful source for other types of information concerning the regulations. A word of caution, however: do not expect the regulatory representative to give you advice or perform services that would be more appropriately provided by a consultant.

Once you have chosen a consultant, a scope of services to specify what will be accomplished should be developed. Usually this will be done by the consultant after he has evaluated your situation. This is an important document that should be reviewed carefully and questioned, if necessary, to be sure it addresses the problem without extraneous work. It should include the development of a timetable to accomplish specific goals and the filing of interim reports to measure progress. If the particular project is going to require approval by the regulatory agency, then the time needed for their review and processing should be included.

If a particular project is going to involve the clean-out and disposal of the contents of a lagoon or tank, there are some practices that should be of interest. One of the most common is the addition of water to sludge to facilitate pumping of the material. In some instances this may be necessary; but it should be minimized, if possible, as you are paying for the transportation and disposal of every gallon of water added. You may find yourself with two million gallons of waste coming out of a one-million-gallon lagoon. The development of large vacuum trucks that can handle a heavy sludge have made this practice less necessary. There is also the opposite situation where a bulking agent is added to a wet material in an attempt to dry it out and make it easier to excavate and load. Again, you are paying to transport and dispose of every pound of bulking agent added to your waste. This situation can usually be avoided by decanting as much liquid as possible off the top of the waste and running it back through the treatment system that generated the sludge.

In summary, be selective when choosing consultants. Try to determine how extensive your problem is; and, after some investigation, select a firm or individual that has experience in handling the entire scope of your problems. Develop a rapport with the representative within the state regulatory agency staff that deals with hazardous waste, and use him or her as your sounding board. Know how your wastes are being handled onsite and offsite, and judge the adequacy of these practices with some knowledge of the requirements and a little common sense.

BIBLIOGRAPHY

"Administrative Procedures for RCRA Permits for Hazardous Waste Facilities," SW-934, U.S. EPA, U.S. Government Printing Office (1981).

"Alternatives to the Land Disposal of Hazardous Wastes—An Assessment for California," Toxic Waste Assessment Group, Governor's Office of Appropriate Technology, Sacramento, CA (1981).

Amstead, B. H., P. Ostwald and M. Begeman. *Manufacturing Processes*, 7th ed. (New York: John Wiley & Sons, Inc., 1977).

"Application for a Hazardous Waste Permit—Consolidated Permits Program," forms 3510-1 and 3510-3, U.S. EPA, U.S. Government Printing Office (1980).

"Assessment of Industrial Hazardous Waste Practices—Electronic Components Manufacturing Industry," SW-140c, U.S. EPA, U.S. Government Printing Office (1977).

"Assessment of Industrial Hazardous Waste Practices: Electroplating and Metal Finishing Industries," SW-136c, U.S. EPA, U.S. Government Printing Office (1977).

"Assessment of Industrial Hazardous Waste Practices: Inorganic Chemicals Industry," SW-104c, U.S. EPA, U.S. Government Printing Office (1975).

"Assessment of Industrial Hazardous Waste Practices: Leather Tanning & Finishing Industry," SW-113c, U.S. EPA, U.S. Government Printing Office (1976).

"Assessment of Industrial Hazardous Waste Practices in the Metal Smelting and Refining Industry," SW 145c.1, U.S. EPA, U.S. Government Printing Office (1977).

"Assessment of Industrial Hazardous Waste Practices: Organic Chemical, Pesticides, and Explosives Industries," SW-118c, U.S. EPA, U.S. Government Printing Office (1977).

"Assessment of Industrial Hazardous Waste Practices: Paint and Allied Products Industry, Contract Solvent Reclaiming Operations, and Factory Application of Coatings, SW-119c, U.S. EPA, U.S. Government Printing Office (1976).

"Assessment of Hazardous Waste Management Practices in the Petroleum Refining Industry," SW-129c, U.S. EPA, U.S. Government Printing Office (1976).

"Assessment of Industrial Hazardous Waste Management Practices: Petroleum Rerefining Industry," SW-144c, U.S. EPA, U.S. Government Printing Office (1977).

"Assessment of Industrial Hazardous Waste Practices: Rubber and Plastics Industry—Vol. II, Plastic Materials and Synthetics Industry," SW-163c.2, U.S. EPA, U.S. Government Printing Office (1978).

"Assessment of Industrial Hazardous Waste Practices: Special Machinery Manufacturing Industries," SW141c, U.S. EPA, U.S. Government Printing Office (1977).

"Assessment of Industrial Hazardous Waste Practices: Storage and Primary Batteries Industries," SW-102c, U.S. EPA, U.S. Government Printing Office (1975).

"Assessment of Industrial Hazardous Waste Practices: Textiles Industry," SW125c, U.S. EPA, U.S. Government Printing Office (1976).

Baker, C. J. *The Firefighter's Handbook of Hazardous Materials,* 3rd ed. (Indianapolis, IN: Maltese Enterprises, Inc., 1972).

"Choosing the Optimum Financial Strategy for Pollution Control Investments," EPA-625/3-76-005, U.S. EPA, U.S. Government Printing Office (1976).

"Choosing Optimum Management Strategies: Pollution Control Systems," EPA-625/3-77-008, U.S. EPA, U.S. Government Printing Office (1977).

Cleaning Our Environment (Homewood, IL: American Chemical Society, 1975).

"Closure and Postclosure: Interim Status Standards," SW-912, 40 CFR 265 (1981).

"Comprehensive Environmental Response, Compensation, and Liability Act of 1980" (PL 96-510), 96th Congress (1980).

"Disposing of Small Batches of Hazardous Wastes," SW-562, U.S. EPA, U.S. Government Printing Office (1976).

Ehlers, V., and E. Steel. *Municipal and Rural Sanitation,* 6th ed. (New York: McGraw-Hill Book Company, 1965).

"EPA/DOT: Hazardous Waste Transportation Interface," SW-935, U.S. EPA, U.S. Government Printing Office (1981).

"Everybody's Problem: Hazardous Waste," SW-826, U.S. EPA, U.S. Government Printing Office (1980).

Federal Register 45(138); 40 CFR 261, pp. 47832-47836.

Federal Register 45(162); 40 CFR 122-124 and 260-265, pp. 55386-55388.

Federal Register 45(197); 40 CFR 264, pp. 66816-66823.

Federal Register 45(212); 40 CFR 260, 261 and 265, pp. 72024-72041.

Federal Register 45(219); 40 CFR 122, p. 74490.

Federal Register 45(220); 40 CFR 261, pp. 74884-74894.

Federal Register 45(223); 40 CFR 122, 260, 264, 265 and 266, pp. 76074-76083.

Federal Register 45(225); 40 CFR 122, 260, 261, 262, 264, 265, pp. 76618-76636.

Federal Register 45(229); 40 CFR 261, 262 and 265, pp. 78524-78550.

Federal Register 45(235); 40 CFR 261, pp. 80286-80287.

Federal Register 45(249); 40 CFR 262 and 263, pp. 85022-85023.

Federal Register 45(252); 40 CFR 122, 263, 264 and 265, pp. 86966-86974.

Federal Register 46(6); 40 CFR 122 and 260, pp. 2344-2348.

Federal Register 46(7); 40 CFR 122, 264 and 265, pp. 2802-2897.

Federal Register 46(9); 40 CFR 260, 261, 262, 264, 265 and 266, pp. 3482-3486.

Federal Register 46(11); 40 CFR 261, pp. 4614-4620.

Federal Register 46(12); 40 CFR 123, pp. 5616-5618.

Federal Register 46(15); 40 CFR 122, 264 and 265, pp. 7666-7690.

Federal Register 46(16); 40 CFR 123, pp. 7964-7966 and 8298-8310; 40 CFR 262, 264 and 265, p. 8395.

Federal Register 46(24); 40 CFR 122, 260 and 264, pp. 11126-11177.

Federal Register 46(27); 40 CFR 122, 260 and 264, p. 11680.

Federal Register 46(30); 40 CFR 122 and 267, pp. 12414-12433.

Federal Register 46(34); 40 CFR 265, pp. 13492-13495.

Federal Register 46(52); 40 CFR 261, pp. 17196-17202.

Federal Register 46(55); 40 CFR 122, 264 and 265, p. 18025.

Federal Register 46(95); 40 CFR 264 and 265, p. 27118.

Federal Register 46(97); 40 CFR 122, 260, 261, 264 and 265, pp. 27473-27480.

Federal Register 46(100); 40 CFR 264, pp. 28314-28328.

Federal Register 46(102); 40 CFR 264, 265 and 267, pp. 28680-28681.

Federal Register 46(106); 40 CFR 162, p. 29708.

Federal Register 46(124); 40 CFR 265, pp. 33502-33507.

Federal Register 46(127); 40 CFR 261, p. 34587.

Federal Register 46(129); 40 CFR 260, 261, 264, 265 and 122, pp. 35246-35249.

Federal Register 46(135); 40 CFR 123 and 124, pp. 36704-36706.

Federal Register 46(139); 40 CFR 264, pp. 37527-37528.

Federal Register 46(142); 40 CFR 122, 264 and 265, pp. 38318-38319.

Federal Register 46(147); 40 CFR 122, 262, 263, 264 and 265, pp. 39426-39429.

Federal Register 46(151); 40 CFR 261, pp. 40154-40167.

Federal Register 46(166); 40 CFR 122 and 146, pp. 43156-43163.

Federal Register 46(173); 40 CFR 261, pp. 44970-44973.

Federal Register 46(186); 40 CFR 261, pp. 47426-47429; 122 and 267, p. 47433.

Federal Register 46(190); 40 CFR 264 and 265, pp. 48197-48198.

Federal Register 46(202); 40 CFR 264, pp. 51407-51410.

Federal Register 46(215); 40 CFR 122 and 264, pp. 55110-55113.

Federal Register 46(221); 40 CFR 261, pp. 56582-56589; 265, pp. 56592-56596.

Federal Register 46(225); 40 CFR 264, pp. 57284-57286.

Federal Register 46(237); 40 CFR 122 and 262, pp. 60446-60448.

Federal Register 47(6); 40 CFR 123 and 262, pp. 1248-1251; 265, pp. 1254-1255.

Federal Register 47(10); 40 CFR 265, p. 2316.

Federal Register 47(22); 40 CFR 122, 260, 264, 265 and 266, pp. 4706-4707.

Federal Register 47(23); 40 CFR 122, pp. 4992-5001.

Federal Register 47(25); 40 CFR 123, pp. 5412-5413.

Federal Register 47(36); 40 CFR 262, 264 and 265, pp. 7841-7842.

Federal Register 47(37); 40 CFR 123, pp. 8010-8011.

Federal Register 47(38); 40 CFR 122, 264 and 265, pp. 8304-8313.

Federal Register 47(40); 40 CFR 265, p. 8606.

Federal Register 47(42); 40 CFR 260, pp. 9007-9008.

Federal Register 47(43); 40 CFR 123, 260 and 262, pp. 9336-9347.

Federal Register 47(44); 40 CFR 265, p. 9803.

Federal Register 47(45); 40 CFR 123, 260 and 262.

Federal Register 47(46); 40 CFR 122, 264 and 265, pp. 10006 and 10059.

Federal Register 47(55); 40 CFR 265, pp. 12316-12318.

Federal Register 47(60); 40 CFR 265, pp. 13173-13174.

Federal Register 47(67); 40 CFR 264 and 265, pp. 15032-15074.

Federal Register 47(68); 40 CFR 122 and 124, pp. 15304-15308.

Federal Register 47(74); 40 CFR 123, 264 and 265, pp. 16544-16561.

Federal Register 47(81); 40 CFR 123, 264 and 265, p. 17989.

Federal Register 47(90); 40 CFR 264 and 265, p. 19995.

"Federal Register: What It Is and How To Use It," Office of the Federal Register, U.S. Government Printing Office (1980).

"Financial Assurance and Liability Insurance: Requirements for Owners and Operators of Hazardous Waste Treatment, Storage, and Disposal Facilities under RCRA, Subtitle C, Subpart H," SW-926, U.S. EPA, U.S. Government Printing Office (1981).

"Financial Requirements: Interim Status Standards," SW-913, 40 CFR 265, Subpart H (1981).

Fundamentals of Industrial Hygiene (Chicago: National Safety Council, 1977).

Greenwood, D. R., et al. "A Handbook of Key Federal Regulations and Criteria for Multimedia Environmental Control," EPA-600/7-79-175, U.S. EPA. U.S. Government Printing Office (1979).

"Guide to the Consolidated Application Form," C-7, U.S. EPA, U.S. Government Printing Office (1979).

"Guide to the Proposed Consolidated Permit Regulations," C-3, U.S. EPA, U.S. Government Printing Office (1979).

"Hazardous Waste: A Guide for Obtaining Permits and Authorization for State Programs," SW-765, U.S. EPA, U.S. Government Printing Office (1979).

"Hazardous Waste Disposal Methods: Major Problems with Their Use," CED-81-21, Report by the Comptroller General of the United States, General Accounting Office (1980).

"Hazardous Waste Generation and Commercial Hazardous Waste Management Capacity—An Assessment," SW-894, U.S. EPA, U.S. Government Printing Office (1980).

"Hazardous Waste Management System: Cooperative Arrangements With States That Are Developing Programs for RCRA Authorization," *Federal Register* 45(99):33784-33786.

Krofchak, D. *Management and Engineering Guide to Economic Pollution Control* (Guelph, Ontario: Go Print G. T. & C. Ltd., 1972).

Manahan, S. E. *Environmental Chemistry*, 3rd ed. (Boston, MA: Williard Grant Press, 1979).

"Material Safety Data Sheet," OSHA 2265, U.S. Department of Labor, Occupational Safety and Health Administration, U.S. Government Printing Office (1977).

Metcalf & Eddy, Inc. *Wastewater Engineering: Collection, Treatment, Disposal* (New York: McGraw-Hill Book Company, 1972).

Metcalf & Eddy, Inc. *Wastewater Engineering: Treatment/Disposal/Reuse*, 2nd ed. (New York: McGraw-Hill Book Company, 1979).

"Method for Determining the Compatibility of Hazardous Wastes," EPA-600/2-80-076, U.S. EPA, U.S. Government Printing Office (1980).

"National Interim Primary Drinking Water Regulations," EPA-570/9-76-003, U.S. EPA, U.S. Government Printing Office (1976).

"Notification of Hazardous Waste Activity," EPA form 8700-12, U.S. EPA, U.S. Government Printing Office (1980).

"Occupational Health Guidelines for Chemical Hazards," NIOSH Publication No. 81-123, National Institute for Occupational Safety and Health, U.S. Government Printing Office (1981).

Parker, H. W. *Air Pollution* (Englewood Cliffs, NJ: Prentice-Hall, Inc., 1977).

PEDCO Environmental. "Mock RCRA Part B Permit Application," U.S. EPA conference, April 6, 1982.

"Pharmaceutical Industry: Hazardous Waste Generation, Treatment, and Disposal," SW-508, U.S. EPA, U.S. Government Printing Office (1976).

"Plans, Recordkeeping, Variances, and Demonstrations for Hazardous Waste Treatment, Storage, and Disposal Facilities, SW-921," U.S. EPA, U.S. Government Printing Office (1981).

"Pocket Guide to Chemical Hazards," NIOSH Publication No. 78-210, National Institute for Occupational Safety and Health, U.S. Government Printing Office (1980).

"Practical Assessment of Industrial Waste Management Strategies," paper presented at the CESOS/CER Company Conference, February 16-18, 1981.

"Preliminary Notification of Hazardous Waste Activity," *Federal Register* 45(39):12746-12754; 40 CFR 260, pp. 12722-12724; 40 CFR 262, pp. 12724-12743; 40 CFR 263, pp. 12743-12744.

"Questions and Answers on Hazardous Waste Regulations," SW-853, U.S. EPA, U.S. Government Printing Office (1980).

"RCRA Inspection Manual," U.S. EPA, U.S. Government Printing Office (1980).

"RCRA Personnel Training Guidance Manual," SW-915, U.S. EPA, U.S. Government Printing Office (1980).

"Regional Guidance Manual for Selected Interim Status Requirements," U.S. EPA, U.S. Government Printing Office (1980).

"Regulation Information for Hazardous Waste Generators and Transporters," SW-906, U.S. EPA, U.S. Government Printing Office (1980).

"Report to Congress: How to Dispose of Hazardous Wastes," CED-79-13, U.S. General Accounting Office, U.S. Government Printing Office (1978).

"Resource Conservation and Recovery Act" (Public Law 94-580), 94th Congress, October 21, 1976, as amended by the Quiet Communities Act of 1978; Solid Waste Disposal Act Amendments of 1980; Used Oil Recycling Act of 1980; and Comprehensive Environmental Response, Compensation, and Liability Act of 1980.

Robbins, R. L., Ed. Proceedings of the Conference on Limiting Liability for Hazardous Waste, Chicago-Kent College of Law, Chicago, IL, November 18-20, 1981.

"Shell Chemical Safety Guide," Shell Chemical Company (1979).

"State Decision-Maker's Guide for Hazardous Waste Management," SW-612, U.S. EPA, U.S. Government Printing Office (1977).

"Summary of Panel Discussions Regarding the Land Disposal of Hazardous Waste," *Federal Register* 46(248):62689 (1981).

Tchobanoglous, G., H. Theisen and R. Eliassen. *Solid Wastes: Engineering Principles and Management Issues* (New York: McGraw-Hill Book Company, 1977).

"Test Methods for Evaluating Solid Waste: Physical/Chemical Methods," SW-846, U.S. EPA, U.S. Government Printing Office (1980).

"Transport of Hazardous Wastes and Hazardous Substances," 49 CFR 171, 172, 173, 174, 176 and 177; and 45 FR 34560-34705 (1980).

Water Quality and Treatment, 3rd ed. (New York: American Water Works Association, 1971).

Woodruff, P. H. "Environmental Compliance Reviews," paper presented at the Mid-Atlantic Industrial Waste Conference, University of Delaware, Newark, DE, April 21, 1982.

U.S. ENVIRONMENTAL PROTECTION AGENCY REGIONAL WASTE MANAGEMENT OFFICES

Region	Area Served	Mailing Address, Telephone
I	Connecticut, Maine, Massachusetts, Rhode Island, Vermont, New Hampshire	U.S. EPA, Region I Waste Management Branch John F. Kennedy Bldg. Boston, MA 02203 (617) 223-5775
II	New Jersey, New York, Virgin Islands, Puerto Rico	U.S. EPA, Region II Solid Waste Branch 26 Federal Plaza New York, NY 10007 (212) 264-0503
III	Delaware, District of Columbia, Maryland, Pennsylvania, Virginia, West Virginia	U.S. EPA, Region III Hazardous Materials Branch 6th and Walnut Sts. Philadelphia, PA 19106 (215) 597-7370
IV	Alabama, Florida, Georgia, Kentucky, Mississippi, North Carolina, South Carolina, Tennessee	U.S. EPA, Region IV Residuals Management Branch 345 Courtland St., N.E. Atlanta, GA 30365 (404) 881-3016
V	Illinois, Indiana, Michigan, Minnesota, Ohio, Wisconsin	U.S. EPA, Region V Waste Management Branch 230 South Dearborn St. Chicago, IL 60604 (312) 353-2917
VI	Arkansas, Louisiana, New Mexico, Oklahoma, Texas	U.S. EPA, Region VI Solid Waste Branch 1201 Elm Street Dallas, TX 75270 (214) 767-2645

Region	Area Served	Mailing Address, Telephone
VII	Iowa, Kansas, Missouri, Nebraska	U.S. EPA, Region VII Hazardous Materials Branch 324 E. 11th Street Kansas City, MO 64108 (816)374-3307
VIII	Colorado, Montana, North Dakota, South Dakota, Utah, Wyoming	U.S. EPA, Region VIII Waste Management Branch 1860 Lincoln St. Denver, CO 80295 (303)837-2221
IX	Arizona, California, Hawaii, Nevada, Guam, American Samoa, Commonwealth of the Northern Marianas	U.S. EPA, Region IX Hazardous Materials Branch 215 Fremont St. San Francisco, CA 94105 (415)556-4606
X	Alaska, Idaho, Oregon, Washington	U.S. EPA, Region X Waste Management Branch 1200 6th Ave. Seattle, WA 98101 (202)442-1260

STATE SOLID WASTE AGENCIES

Alabama

Alfred S. Chipley (S, H)*
Division of Solid Waste and Vector
  Control
Department of Public Health, Rm.
  1212
Union Bank Building
Montgomery, AL 36130
(205)832-6728/(205)834-1303

Alaska

Alan Boggs (S)
Air & Solid Waste Management
Department of Environmental
  Conservation
Pouch O
Juneau, AK 99811
(907)465-2635

David Ditraglia, Director (H)
Air & Solid Waste Management
Department of Environmental
  Conservation
Pouch O
Juneau, AK 99811
(907)465-2687

Arizona

Tibaldo Canez, Bureau Chief (S, H)
Department of Health Services
1740 West Adams St.

Phoenix, AZ 85008
(602)255-1170

Arkansas

Jim Beardon, Assistant Chief (S)
Solid Waste Division
Department of Pollution Control and
  Ecology
8001 National Drive
Little Rock, AR 72219

Wilson Folefree (H)
Air & Hazardous Waste Division
Department of Pollution Control &
  Ecology
8001 National Drive
Little Rock, AR 72219
(501)371-1135

California

Terry Trumlull, Chairman (S)
State Solid Waste Management Board
1020 9th St., Suite 300
Sacramento, CA 95814
(916)322-3330

Peter A. Rogers, Chief (H)
Hazardous Waste Management
  Branch
Department of Health Services
714/744 P St.
Sacramento, CA 95814
(916)322-2337

*S = solid waste management contact; H = hazardous waste management contact.

Colorado

Orville Stoddard (S)
Senior Public Health
Colorado Department of Health
4210 E. 11th Ave.
Denver, CO 80220
(303)320-8333

Ken Waesche, Division Director (H)
Waste Management Division
Department of Health
4210 E. 11th Ave.
Denver, CO 80220
(303)320-8333

Connecticut

Charles Kurker, Director (S)
Solid Waste Management Unit
Dept. of Environmental Protection
165 Capitol Ave.
Hartford, CT 06115
(203)566-3672

Stephen Hitchcock, Director (H)
Hazardous Waste Mgmt. Unit
Department of Environmental
    Protection
165 Capitol Ave.
Hartford, CT 06115
(203)566-5148

Patrick F. Bowe (H)
Hazardous Materials Mgmt. Unit
Dept. of Environmental Protection
165 Capitol Ave.
Hartford, CT 06115
(203)566-5712

Delaware

Kenneth R. Weiss, Supervisor (S, H)
Sold Waste Management Section
Dept. of Natural Resources and
    Environ. Control
Edward Tatnall Bldg.
P.O. Box 1401
Dover, DE 19901
(302)736-4781

District of Columbia

Malcolm Hope
Dept. of Environ. Services
415 12th St., N.W., Rm. 308
Washington, DC 20004
(202)727-5701

Florida

Bob McVety, Chairman (S, H)
Solid Waste Management Prg.
Dept. of Environmental Regulation
Twin Towers Off. Bldg.
2600 Blair Stone Rd., Rm. 421
Tallahassee, FL 32301
(904)488-0300

Robert Hawfield (H)
Hazardous Waste Division
Dept. of Environmental Regulation
Twin Towers Office Bldg.
2600 Blair Stone Rd.
Tallahassee, FL 32301
(904)488-0300

Georgia

Moses N. McCall, III, Chief (S, H)
Land Protection Branch
Environmental Protection Division
Department of Natural Resources
270 Washington St., SW, Rm. 822
Atlanta, GA 30334
(404)656-2833

John Taylor, Program Manager (H)
Industrial & Hazardous Waste
    Management Program
Land Protection Branch
Environmental Protection Division
Department of Natural Resources
270 Washington St., SW
Atlanta, GA 30344
(404)767-2833

Hawaii

Melvin Koizumi, Dep. Director
    (S, H)
Environmental Health Div.
Department of Health
P.O. Box 3378
Honolulu, HI 96801
(808)548-4139

Idaho

Robert P. Olsen (S, H)
Hazardous Materials Bureau
Department of Health and Welfare
State House
Boise, ID 83720
(208)334-4108

Illinois

Bob Kuykendall (S, H)
Division of Land and Noise Pollution
   Control
Environmental Prot. Agency
2200 Churchill Rd., Rm. A104
Springfield, IL 62706
(217)782-6760

Indiana

David Lamm, Director (S)
Land Pollution Control Division
State Board of Health
1330 W. Michigan St., Rm. A304
Indianapolis, IN 46206
(317)633-0176

Guinn Doyle, Chief (H)
Hazardous Waste Management
   Branch
Land Pollution Control Division
State Board of Health
1330 W. Michigan St., Rm. A304
Indianapolis, IN 46206
(317)633-0178

Iowa

Charles C. Miller, Dir. (S, H)
Air and Land Quality Div.
Dept. of Envir. Quality
Henry A. Wallace Bldg.
900 E. Grand St., 3rd fl.
Des Moines, IA 50319
(515)281-8853

Kansas

Charles H. Linn, Chief (S)
Solid Waste Mgmt. Section
Dept. of Health and Envir.
Forbes Field, Bldg. 321
Topeka, KS 66620
(913)862-9390 x297

John Paul Goetz, Chief (H)
Hazardous Waste Management Unit
Department of Health and
   Environment
Forbes Field
Topeka, KS 66620
(913)862-9360

Kentucky

Carl Schroeder (S)
Division of Hazardous Materials &
   Waste Management
Dept. of Natural Resources &
   Environmental Protection
1121 Louisville Rd.
Pineville Plaza
Frankfort, KY 40601
(502)564-6716

Alex Barber (H)
Division of Hazardous Materials &
   Waste Management
Department of Natural Resources &
   Environmental Protection
1121 Louisville Rd.
Pineville Plaza
Frankfort, KY 40601
(502)564-6716

Louisiana

Gerald Healy, Jr., Administrator
   (S, H)
Hazardous Waste Management
   Division
Department of Natural Resources
P.O. Box 44066
Baton Rouge, LA 70804
(504)342-1255/(504)342-1227

Louisiana—*continued*

James Hutchinson, Deputy Secretary
(*H*)
Department of Natural Resources
P.O. Box 44396
Baton Rouge, LA 70804
(504)342-4506

Maine

Florence Hoar, Acting Director (*S*)
Waste Management Division
Department of Environmental
  Protection
State House
Augusta, ME 04333
(207)289-2111

John Brochu, Director (*H*)
Bureau of Oil & Hazardous Waste
  Materials
Department of Environmental
  Protection
State House, Station 17
Augusta, ME 04333
(207)289-3355

Maryland

Ronald Nelson, Director (*S, H*)
Waste Management Administration
Office of Environmental Programs
Department of Health & Mental
  Hygiene
201 W. Preston St., Rm. 212
Baltimore, MD 21201
(301)383-3123/(301)383-2771

Massachusetts

William Cass, Director (*S, H*)
Division of Hazardous Waste
Department of Environmental Quality
  Engineering
One Winter St.
Boston, MA 02108
(617)727-5431

Michigan

Fred Kellow, Division Chief (*S*)
Resource Recovery Division
Department of Natural Resources
Westland Plaza
Lansing, MI 48909
(517)373-0540

Delbert Rector, Acting Chief (*H*)
Office of Hazardous Waste
  Management
Environmental Services Division
Department of Natural Resources
P.O. Box 30028
Lansing, MI 48909
(517)373-3560

David Dennis, Chief (*H*)
Oil & Hazardous Materials Control
  Section
Water Quality Division
Department of Natural Resources
P.O. Box 30028
Lansing, MI 48909
(517)373-2794

Minnesota

Dale L. Wikre, Director (*S, H*)
Division of Solid and Hazardous
  Waste
Pollution Control Agency
1935 W. County Rd., B-2
Roseville, MN 55113
(612)297-2735

Mississippi

Jack M. McMillan, Director (*S, H*)
Division of Solid Waste Mgmt. and
  Vector Control
Department of Natural Resources
P.O. Box 10385
Jackson, MS 39209
(601)961-5062/(601)961-5171

Missouri

David Bedan (S, H)
Solid Waste Management Program
Department of Natural Resources
State Office Building
P.O. Box 1368
Jefferson City, MO 65102
(314)751-3241

Montana

Duane L. Robertson, Chief (S, H)
Solid Waste Management Bureau
Department of Health and
    Environmental Sciences
Cogswell Bldg., Rm. A201
Helena, MT 59601
(406)449-2821

Nebraska

Maurice W. Sheil, Chief (S, H)
Solid Waste Division
Department of Environmental Control
State House Station
301 Centennial Mall South
Lincoln, NE 68509
(402)471-2186

Nevada

Lewis H. Dodgin, Administrator
    (S, H)
Division of Environmental Protection
Department of Conservation and
    Natural Resources
Capital Complex
Carson City, NV 89710
(702)885-4670

New Hampshire

Thomas L. Sweeney, Chief (S, H)
Bureau of Solid Waste
Department of Health and Welfare
Health and Welfare Building
Hazen Drive
Concord, NH 03301
(603)271-4610

New Jersey

Lino F. Pereira, Administrator (S, H)
Solid Waste Administration
Division of Environmental Quality
P.O. Box CNO27
Trenton, NJ 08625
(609)292-9120

New Mexico

Dr. Ray Krehoff, Program Manager
    (S, H)
Solid & Hazardous Waste
    Management Program
Community Support Services Section
Health and Environment Department
P.O. Box 968
Santa Fe, NM 87503
(505)872-5271 x282

New York

Norman H. Nosenchuck, Director
    (S, H)
Division of Solid Waste
Department of Environmental
    Conservation
50 Wolf Rd., Rm. 415
Albany, NY 12233
(518)457-6603

William Wilkie, Assistant Director
    (H)
Division of Solid Waste
Department of Environmental
    Conservation
50 Wolf Rd., Rm. 415
Albany, NY 12233
(418)457-6603

North Carolina

O. W. Strickland, Head (S, H)
Solid & Hazardous Waste
    Management Branch
Division of Health Services
Department of Human Resources
P.O. Box 2091
Raleigh, NC 27602
(919)733-2178

North Dakota

Jay Crawford, Director (S, H)
Division of Environmental Waste
    Mgmt. and Research
Department of Health
1200 Missouri Ave., 3rd fl.
Bismarck, ND 58505
(701)224-2382/(701)224-2392

Ohio

Donald E. Day, Chief (S)
Office of Land Pollution Control
Environmental Protection Agency
P.O. Box 1049
Columbus, OH 43216
(614)466-8934

Charles Wilhelm, Chief (H)
Office of Hazardous Materials
    Management
Ohio Environmental Protection
    Agency
361 E. Broad St.
Columbus, OH 43215
(514)466-8934

Ken Schultz (H)
Office of Emergency Response
Ohio Environmental Protection
    Agency
361 E. Broad St.
Columbus, OH 43215
(614)466-8934

Oklahoma

H. A. Caves, Chief (S, H)
Industrial and Solid Waste Service
Department of Health
1000 NE 10th St., Rm. 803
P.O. Box 53551
Oklahoma City, OK 73152
(405)271-5338

Oregon

Ernest A. Schmidt, Administrator
    (S, H)
Solid Waste Mgmt. Division
Dept. of Environmental Quality
522 SW Fifth Ave.
P.O. Box 1760
Portland, OR 97204
(503)229-5913

Pennsylvania

Donald A. Lazarchik (S, H)
Bureau of Solid Waste Management
Department of Environmental
    Resources
Fulton Building, 8th fl.
P.O. Box 2063
Harrisburg, PA 17120
(717)787-9870

Gary Galida, Chief (H)
Division of Hazardous Waste
    Management
Bureau of Solid Waste Management
Department of Environmental
    Resources
Fulton Building, 8th fl.
P.O. Box 2063
Harrisburg, PA 17120
(717)787-7381

Rhode Island

John S. Quinn, Jr., Chief (S, H)
Solid Waste Management Program
Department of Environmental
    Management
204 Cannon Building
75 Davis St.
Providence, RI 02098
(401)277-2808

Lou David, Jr., Exec. Director (S, H)
Attention: Russ Carlson
Rhode Island Solid Waste Corp.
39 Pike St.
Providence, RI 02903
(401)831-4440

South Carolina

Robert Malpass, Chief (S, H)
Bureau of Solid and Hazardous Waste
    Management
Department of Health and
    Environmental Control
J. Marion Simms Building
2600 Bull St.
Columbia, SC 29201
(803)758-5681

South Dakota

Joel C. Smith (S, H)
Air Quality and Solid Waste Prg.
Department of Health
Joe Foss Bldg.
Pierre, SD 57501
(605)773-3329

Tennessee

Tom Tiesler, Director (S, H)
Div. of Solid Waste Management
Bureau of Environmental Services
Department of Public Health
Capitol Hill Bldg., Suite 326
Nashville, TN 37219
(615)741-3424

Texas

Jack C. Carmichael, Chief (S, H)
Bureau of Solid Waste Management
Department of Health
1100 West 49th St., T-602
Austin, TX 78756
(512)458-7111/(512)475-2041

Jay Snow, Head (H)
Industrial Solid Waste Unit
Department of Water Resources
1700 North Congress, Rm. 237-1
P.O. Box 13087, Capitol Station
Austin, TX 78711
(512)475-2041

Utah

Dale Parker, Director (S, H)
Bur. of Solid Waste Management
Division of Health
150 West North Temple
P.O. Box 2500
Salt Lake City, UT 84101
(801)533-4145

Vermont

Richard A. Valentinetti, Chief (S, H)
Air and Solid Waste Programs
Agency of Environmental
    Conservation
State Office Building
Montpelier, VT 05602
(802)828-3395

John Malter, Chief (H)
Hazardous Materials Management
    Section
Agency of Environmental
    Conservation
State Office Building
Montpelier, VT 05602
(802)828-3395

Virginia

William F. Gilley, Director (S, H)
Bureau of Solid and Hazardous Waste
    Management
Department of Health
Madison Bldg., Rm. 927
109 Governor St.
Richmond, VA 23219
(804)786-5271

Washington

Earl Tower, Supervisor (S, H)
Solid Waste Management Division
Office of Land Programs
Department of Ecology
Mail Stop PV-11
Olympia, WA 89504
(206)753-4276/(206)459-6317

Washington—*continued*

Tom Cook, Section Head (*H*)
Hazardous Waste Section
Department of Ecology
Olympia, WA 98504
(206)753-4276

West Virginia

Dale Parsons, Director (*S, H*)
Solid Waste Division
Department of Health
1800 Washington St. E, Rm. 520
Charleston, WV 25305
(304)348-2987

John Northeimer (*H*)
Division of Water Resources
Dept. of Natural Resources
1201 Greenbrier St., 2nd fl.
Charleston, WV 25311
(304)348-0375

Wisconsin

Robert Krill, Director (*S, H*)
Bureau of Waste Management
Dept. of Natural Resources
P.O. Box 7921
Madison, WI 53702
(608)266-1327

Wyoming

Charles Porter, Supervisor (*S*)
Solid Waste Management Program
State of Wyoming
Dept. of Environmental Quality
Equality State Bank Building
401 W. 19th St., Rm. 3011
Cheyenne, WY 82002
(307)777-7752

Courtesy of the Association of State and Territorial Solid Waste Management Officials.

EXAMPLES OF
POTENTIALLY INCOMPATIBLE WASTES

Many hazardous wastes, when mixed with other waste or materials at a hazardous waste facility, can produce effects that are harmful to human health and the environment, such as (1) heat or pressure, (2) fire or explosion, (3) violent reaction, (4) toxic dusts, mists, fumes or gases, or (5) flammable fumes or gases.

Below are examples of potentially incompatible wastes, waste components and materials, along with the harmful consequences that result from mixing materials in one group with materials in another group. The list is intended as a guide to owners or operators of treatment, storage and disposal facilities, and to enforcement and permit granting officials, to indicate the need for special precautions when managing these potentially incompatible waste materials or components.

This list is not intended to be exhaustive. An owner or operator must, as the regulations require, adequately analyze his wastes so that he can avoid creating uncontrolled substances or reactions of the type listed below, whether they are listed below or not.

It is possible for potentially incompatible wastes to be mixed in a way that precludes a reaction (e.g., adding acid to water rather than water to acid) or that neutralizes them (e.g., a strong acid mixed with a strong base), or that controls substances produced (e.g., by generating flammable gases in a closed tank equipped so that ignition cannot occur, and burning the gases in an incinerator).

In the lists below, the mixing of a Group A material with a Group B material may have the potential consequence as noted.

*Source: "Law, Regulations, and Guidelines for Handling of Hazardous Waste," California Department of Health (1975), as referenced in Appendix V of 40 CFR 265.

Group 1-A

Acetylene sludge
Alkaline caustic liquids
Alkaline cleaner
Alkaline corrosive liquids
Alkaline corrosive battery fluid
Caustic wastewater
Lime sludge and other corrosive
    alkalies
Lime wastewater
Lime and water
Spent caustic

Group 1-B

Acid sludge
Acid and water
Battery acid
Chemical cleaners
Electrolyte, acid
Etching acid liquid or solvent
Pickling liquor and other corrosive
    acids
Spent acid
Spent mixed acid
Spent sulfuric acid

Potential consequences: heat generation; violent reaction.

Group 2-A

Aluminum
Beryllium
Calcium
Lithium
Magnesium
Potassium
Sodium
Zinc powder
Other reactive metals and metal
    hydrides

Group 2-B

Any waste in Group 1-A or 1-B

Potential consequences: fire or explosion; generation of flammable hydrogen gas.

Group 3-A

Alcohols
Water

Group 3-B

Any concentrated waste in Groups
    1-A or 1-B
Calcium
Lithium
Metal hydrides
Potassium
SO_2Cl_2, $SOCl_2$, PCl_3, CH_3SiCl_3
Other water-reactive waste

Potential consequences: fire, explosion or heat generation; generation of flammable or toxic gases.

Group 4-A	Group 4-B
Alcohols	Concentrated Group 1-A or 1-B
Aldehydes	wastes
Halogenated hydrocarbons	Group 2-A wastes
Nitrated hydrocarbons	
Unsaturated hydrocarbons	
Other reactive organic compounds and solvents	

Potential consequences: fire, explosion or violent reaction.

Group 5-A	Group 5-B
Spent cyanide and sulfide solutions	Group 1-B wastes

Potential consequences: Generation of toxic hydrogen cyanide or hydrogen sulfide gas.

Group 6-A	Group 6-B
Chlorates	Acetic acid and other organic acids
Chlorine	Concentrated mineral acids
Chlorites	Group 2-A wastes
Chromic acid	Group 4-A wastes
Hypochlorites	Other flammable and combustible
Nitrates	wastes
Nitric acid, fuming	
Perchlorates	
Permanganates	
Peroxides	
Other strong oxidizers	

Potential consequences: fire, explosion or violent reaction.

Appendix 4

INDUSTRIAL WASTE EXCHANGES*

California

California Waste Exchange
Dr. Paul H. Williams
Department of Health Services
Hazardous Materials Management
   Section
2151 Berkeley Way
Berkeley, CA 94704
(415)540-2043

World Association for Solid Waste
   Transfer and Exchange
Frank S. Patrinostra
WASTE
152 Utah Avenue "F"
South San Francisco, CA 94080
(415)871-1711

Zero Waste Systems Inc.
Dr. Paul Palmer
2928 Poplar Street
Oakland, CA 94608
(415)893-8257

Colorado

Colorado Waste Exchange
Olie Webb
Colorado Association of Commerce
   and Industry
1390 Logan
Denver, CO 80203
(303)831-7411

Connecticut

World Association for Safe Transfer
   and Exchange
(WASTE)
Marcel Veroneau
130 Freight St.
Waterbury, CT 06702
(203)574-2463

Florida

Florida Waste Information Exchange
Ray C. Herndon
Florida Chamber of Commerce
P.O. Box 5497
Tallahassee, FL 32301
(904)644-5516

Iso-Chem Marketing Inc.
Anthony L. Tripi
P.O. Box 1268
449 Kingsley Ave.
Orange Park, FL 32073
(904)264-0070

Georgia

Georgia Waste Exchange
Bert Fridlin
Georgia Business & Industry
   Association
181 Washington St. SW
Atlanta, GA 30303
(404)659-4444

*Sources: Moore, L. E. "Industrial Waste Exchanges," *Poll. Eng.* (January 1982),
p. 33. "Waste Exchanges—Background Information," SW-887.1, U.S. Government
Printing Office (1980).

Illinois

American Chemical Exchange (ACE)
Tom Hurvis
4849 Golf Rd.
Skokie, IL
(312)677-2800

Environmental Clearinghouse
   Organization (ECHO)
William Petrich
3426 Maple Ln.
Hazel Crest, IL 60429
(312)335-0754

Industrial Material Exchange Service
Larry Moore
Illinois EPA
Division of Land/Noise
2200 Churchill Rd.
Springfield, IL 62706
(217)782-9800

Indiana

Waste Materials Clearinghouse
Environmental Quality Control Inc.
Noble L. Beck
1220 Waterway Blvd.
Indianapolis, IN 46202
(317)634-2142

Iowa

Iowa Industrial Waste Information
   Exchange
Edward O. Sealine
Center for Industrial Research &
   Service
201 Building E
Iowa State University
Ames, IA 50011
(515)294-3420

Kentucky

Louisville Area Waste Exchange
Stanford Lampe
300 West Liberty St.
Louisville, KY 40202
(502)582-2421

Maine

Peck Environmental Laboratory
Dana Peck
P.O. Box 947
Kennebunk, ME 04047
(207)985-6116

Massachusetts

The Exchange
Howell Hurst
63 Rutland St.
Boston, MA 02118
(617)367-2334 or 367-0810

Michigan

American Materials Exchange
   Network
Vewiser Dixon
19489 Lahser Rd.
Detroit, MI 48219
(313)532-7900

Minnesota

Minnesota Association of Commerce
   and Industry Waste Exchange
   Service
James T. Shields
Minnesota Association for Commerce
   and Industry
200 Hanover Building
480 Cedar St.
St. Paul, MN 55101
(612)227-9591

Missouri

Midwest Industrial Waste Exchange
Oscar S. Richards
10 Broadway
St. Louis, MO 63102
(312)231-5555

New Hampshire

Resource Conservation and Recovery
Agency
David Green
P.O. Box 268
Stratham, NH 03885
(603)772-6261

New Jersey

Industrial Waste Information
Exchange
New Jersey State Chamber of
Commerce
5 Commerce St.
Newark, NJ 07102
(201)623-7070

New York

Enkarn Research Corporation
J. T. Engster
P.O. Box 590
Albany, NY 12201
(518)436-9684

Manufacturers Association of Central
New York
Stephen Hoefer
770 James St.
Syracuse, NY 13203
(315)474-4201

Northeast Industrial Waste Exchange
Walker Banning
700 East Water St.
Syracuse, NY 13210
(315)422-8276

The American Alliance of Resources
Recovery Interests Inc. (AARRII)
John Flandreau
111 Washington Ave.
Albany, NY 12210
(518)436-1557

North Carolina

The Piedmont Exchange
Mary Dawn Liston
Institute for Urban Studies, UNCC
Charlotte, NC 28223
(704)597-2307

Atlantic Coast Exchange
Brian Aus
Research Triangle Operations
1905 Chapel Hill Rd.
Durham, NC 27707
(919)493-3536

Ohio

Ore Corporation
Ohio Resource Exchange
Richard L. Immerman
2415 Woodmere Dr.
Cleveland, OH 44106
(216)371-4869

Oregon

Oregon Industrial Waste Information
Exchange
David Clark
Western Environmental Trade
Association
333 SW 5th, Suite 618
Portland, OR 97204
(503)221-0357

Pennsylvania

National Waste Exchange (NWX)
Ron Schaible
P.O. Box 190
Silver Springs, PA 17575
(717)780-6189

Pennsylvania Waste Information
Exchange
Tricia Overmeyer
Pennsylvania Chamber of Commerce
222 North Third St.
Harrisburg, PA 17101
(717)255-3279 or 255-3252

Tennessee

Tennessee Waste Swap
Nancy Niemeier
Tennessee Manufacturers Association
708 Fidelity Federal Building
Nashville, TN 37219
(615)256-5141

Texas

Chemical Recycle Information
    Program
Jack Westney
Houston Chamber of Commerce
1100 Milam Building, 25th fl.
Houston, TX 77002
(713)651-1313

Utah

Inter-Mountain Waste Exchange
W. S. Hatch Co.
P.O. Box 1825
Salt Lake City, UT 84110
(801)295-5511

Washington

Information Center for Waste
    Exchange
Judy Henry
2112 Third Ave., Suite 303
Seattle, WA 98121
(206)623-5235

Appendix 5

RESOURCE CONSERVATION AND RECOVERY ACT INSPECTION REPORT: U.S. ENVIRONMENTAL PROTECTION AGENCY REGION V

EPA Identification Number: __ __ __   __ __ __ __ __ __ __ __ __

Installation Name: _____

Location Address: _____

City: _____   State: _____

Date of inspection: _____   Time of inspection (from) _____ (to) _____

Person(s) interviewed   Title   Telephone

_____   _____   _____

_____   _____   _____

_____   _____   _____

Inspector(s)   Agency/Title   Telephone

_____   _____   _____

_____   _____   _____

Installation Activity (mark only one box)   Inspection Form(s)

Ⅱ Treatment/Storage/Disposal per 40 CFR 265.1 and
   Generation and/or Transportation   A

Ⅱ Treatment/Storage/Disposal (no generation or Transportation)   A

Ⅱ Generation and Transportation   B, C

Ⅱ Generation only   B

Ⅱ Transportation only   C

253

INSPECTION FORM A

Section A: SCOPE OF INSPECTION.

1. Interim status standards for treatment storage or disposal of HAZARDOUS
    WASTES SUBJECT TO 40 CFR 265.1. Complete Inspection Form A sections B, C,
    D, E, and G.

2. Place an "X" in the box(es) corresponding to the facility's treatment,
    storage and disposal processes, and generation and/or transportation
    activity (if any). Complete only the applicable sections and appendixes.

Permit application process(es) (EPA Form 3510-3)   Inspection Form A section(s)

S01 ☐	storage in containers	I
S02 ☐	storage in tanks	J
T01 ☐	treatment in tanks	J
S04 ☐	storage in surface impoundment	K,F
T02 ☐	treatment in surface impoundment	K,F
D83 ☐	disposal in surface impoundment	K,F
S03 ☐	storage in waste pile	L
D81 ☐	disposal by land application	M,F
D80 ☐	disposal in landfill	N,F
T03 ☐	treatment by incineration	O/P
T04 ☐	treatment in devices other than tanks, surface impoundments, or incinerators	Q

Other activities

GENERATOR ☐	APPENDIX	GN
TRANSPORTER ☐	APPENDIX	TR

3. Indicate any hazardous waste processes, by process code, which have been
    omitted from Part A of the facility's permit application.

4. Indicate any hazardous waste processes (by process code and line number on
    EPA Form 3510-3 page 1 of 5) which appear to be eligible for exclusion per
    40 CFR 265.1(c). Provide a brief rationale for the possible exclusion.

A-1   (4-82A)

Section B: GENERAL FACILITY STANDARDS: (Part 265 Subpart B)

			YES	NO	NI*	Remarks

1. Has the Regional Administrator
   been notified regarding:

   a. Receipt of hazardous
   waste from a foreign source?   ___ ___ ___ _____

   b. Facility expansion?   ___ ___ ___ _____

   c. Change of owner or operator?   ___ ___ ___ _____

2. General Waste Analysis:

   a. Has the owner or operator obtained
   a detailed chemical and physical
   analysis of the waste?   ___ ___ ___ _____

   b. Does the owner or operator have
   a detailed waste analysis plan
   on file at the facility?   ___ ___ ___ _____

   c. Does the waste analysis plan
   specify procedures for inspection
   and analysis of each movement of
   hazardous waste from off-site?   ___ ___ ___ _____

3. Security - Do security measures include:
   (if applicable)

   a. 24-Hour surveillance?   ___ ___ ___ _____
      or
   b. i. Artificial or natural
   barrier around facility?   ___ ___ ___ _____
     and
   ii. Controlled entry?   ___ ___ ___ _____

   c. Danger sign(s) at
   entrance?   ___ ___ ___ _____

4. Owner or operator inspections:

   a. Does the owner or operator
   inspect the facility for
   malfunctions, deterioration,
   operator errors, and discharges
   of hazardous waste that
   may affect human health or
   the environment?   ___ ___ ___ _____

*Not Inspected

	YES	NO	NI	Remarks

b. Does the owner or operator
have an inspection schedule
at the facility?

c. If so, does the schedule address
the inspection of the following
items:

   i. monitoring equipment?

   ii. safety and emergency equipment?

  iii. security devices?

   iv. operating and structural equipment (i.e. dikes, pumps, etc.)?

   v. type of problems to be looked
for during the inspection (e.g.
leaky fitting, defective pump,
etc.)?

   vi. inspection frequency (based upon
the possible deterioration rate
of the equipment)?

d. Are areas subject to spills inspected daily when in use?

e. Does the owner or operator maintain
an inspection log or summary of
owner or operator inspections?

f. Does the inspection log contain the
following information:

   i. the date and time of the inspection?

   ii. the name of the inspector?

  iii. a notation of the observations
made?

   iv. the date and nature of any
repairs or remedial actions?

5. Do personnel training records
include:

  a. Job titles?

  b. Job descriptions?

	YES	NO	NI	Remarks

c. Description of training? ___ ___ ___ _____

d. Records of training? ___ ___ ___ _____

e. Did facility personnel receive the required training by 5-19-81? ___ ___ ___ _____

f. Do new personnel receive required training within six months? ___ ___ ___ _____

g. Do personnel training records indicate that personnel have taken part in an annual review of initital training? ___ ___ ___ _____

6. If required, are the following special requirements for ignitable, reactive, or incompatible wastes addressed?

a. Special handling? ___ ___ ___ _____

b. No smoking signs? ___ ___ ___ _____

c. Separation and protection from ignition sources? ___ ___ ___ _____

258   APPENDIX

Section C: PREPAREDNESS AND PREVENTION: (Part 265 Subpart C)

1. Maintenance and Operation
    of Facility:

                                      YES NO   NI   Remarks

    Is there any evidence of fire,
    explosion, or release of
    hazardous waste or hazardous
    waste constituent?   ___ ___ ___   _____

2. If required, does the facility
    have the following equipment:

    a. Internal communications or
        alarm systems?   ___ ___ ___   _____

    b. Telephone or 2-way radios
        at the scene of operations? ___ ___ ___   _____

    c. Portable fire extinguishers,
        fire control, spill control
        equipment and decontamination
        equipment?   ___ ___ ___   _____

    Indicate the volume of water and/or foam available for fire control:

    _____

    _____

3. Testing and Maintenance of
    Emergency Equipment:

    a. Has the owner or operator
        established testing and
        maintenance procedures
        for emergency equipment?   ___ ___ ___   _____

    b. Is emergency equipment
        maintained in operable
        condition?   ___ ___ ___   _____

4. Has owner or operator provided
    immediate access to internal
    alarms? (if needed)   ___ ___ ___   _____

5. Is there adequate aisle space
    for unobstructed movement?   ___ ___ ___   _____

6. Has the owner or operator attempted
    to make arrangements with local
    authorities in case of an emergency
    at the facility?   ___ ___ ___   _____

Section D: CONTINGENCY PLAN AND EMERGENCY PROCEDURES: (Part 265 Subpart D)

	YES	NO	NI	Remarks

1. Does the Contingency Plan contain the
    following information:

    a. The actions facility personnel
        must take to comply with
        §265.51 and 265.56 in response
        to fires, explosions, or any
        unplanned release of hazardous
        waste? (If the owner has a Spill
        Prevention, Control, and Counter-
        measures (SPCC) Plan, he needs
        only to amend that plan to
        incorporate hazardous waste
        management provisions that are
        sufficient to comply with the
        requirements of this Part (as
        applicable.)   ___ ___ ___   _____

    b. Arrangements agreed by local
        police departments, fire departments
        hospitals, contractors, and State
        and local emergency response teams
        to coordinate emergency services
        pursuant to §265.37?   ___ ___ ___   _____

    c. Names, addresses, and phone
        numbers (office and home) of all
        persons qualified to act as
        emergency coordinators?   ___ ___ ___   _____

    d. A list of all emergency equipment
        at the facility which includes the
        location and physical description
        of each item on the list and a
        brief outline of its capabilities? ___ ___ ___   _____

    e. An evacuation plan for facility per-
        sonnel where there is a possibil-
        ity that evacuation could be neces-
        sary? (This plan must describe
        signal(s) to be used to begin evacua-
        tion, evacuation routes, and alternate
        evacuation routes?)   ___ ___ ___   _____

2. Are copies of the Contingency Plan
    available at the site and local
    emergency organizations?   ___ ___ ___   _____

D-1

	YES	NO	NI	Remarks

3. Emergency Coordinator

   a. Is the facility Emergency
      Coordinator identified?   ___ ___ ___   _____

   b. Is coordinator familiar with
      all aspects of site operation
      and emergency procedures?   ___ ___ ___   _____

   c. Does the Emergency Coordinator
      have the authority to carry out
      the Contingency Plan?   ___ ___ ___   _____

4. Emergency Procedures

If an emergency situation has occurred
at this facility, has the Emergency
Coordinator followed the emergency
procedures listed in 265.56?   ___ ___ ___   _____

D-2

4/82-A

Section E: MANIFEST SYSTEM, RECORDKEEPING, AND REPORTING: (Part 265 Subpart E)

	YES	NO	NI	Remarks

** 1.   Use of Manifest System

    a.   Does the facility follow the procedures listed in §265.71 for processing each manifest? (Particularly sending a copy of the signed manifest back to the generator within 30 days after delivery.)

    b.   Are records of past shipments retained for 3 years?

** 2.   Does the owner or operator meet requirements regarding manifest discrepancies?

** Not applicable to owners or operators of on-site facilities that do not receive any waste from off-site sources.

    3.   Operating Record

    a.   Does the owner or operator maintain an operating record as required in 265.73?

    b.   Does the operating record contain the following information:

      i.   The method(s) and date(s) of each waste's treatment, storage, or disposal as required in 40 CFR Part 265 Appendix I?

      ii.   The location and quantity of each hazardous waste within the facility? (This information should be cross-referenced to specific manifest number, if waste was accompanied by by a manifest.)

    ***iii.   A map or diagram of each cell or disposal area

*** only applies to disposal facilities   E-1   4/82-A

	YES	NO	NI	Remarks

showing the location and
quantity of each hazardous
waste? (This information
should be cross-referenced
to specific manifest
number, if waste was
accompanied by a manifest.) — — —   _____

iv. Records and results of all
waste analyses, trial tests,
monitoring data, and operator
inspections? — — —   _____

v. Reports detailing all
incidents that required
implementation of the
Contingency Plan? — — —   _____

vi. All closure and post closure
costs as applicable? — — —   _____

4. Availability of Records

Are all facility records required
under 40 CFR Part 265 available for
inspection? — — —   _____

5.**Unmanifested Waste Reports

a. Has the facility accepted any
hazardous waste from an off-site
generator subject to 40 CFR 262.20
without a manifest or or shipping
paper? — — —   _____

b. If "a" is yes, provide the identity
of the source of the waste and a
description of the quantity, type,
and date received for each unmanifested hazardous waste shipment.   _____
    _____

** Not applicable to owners or operators of on-site facilities that do not receive
any hazardous from off-site sources.

Section G - CLOSURE AND POST CLOSURE (Part 265 Subpart G)

	YES	NO	NI	Remarks

1. Closure

   a. Is the facility closure plan available for inspection? _____ _____ _____ _____

   b. Does the plan identify:

      i. maximum extent unclosed during facility life? _____ _____ _____ _____

      ii. maximum hazardous waste inventory? _____ _____ _____ _____

      iv. estimated year of closure? _____ _____ _____ _____

      v. schedule of closure activities? _____ _____ _____ _____

   c. Has closure begun? _____ _____ _____ _____

*2. Post-Closure

   a. Is the post-closure plan available for inspection? _____ _____ _____ _____

   b. Does this plan contain:

      i. description of groundwater monitoring activities and frequencies? _____ _____ _____ _____

      ii. description of maintenance activities and frequencies for

         AA. integrity of cap, final cover, or containment structures, where applicable _____ _____ _____ _____

         BB. facility monitoring equipment _____ _____ _____ _____

      iii. name, address, and phone number of person or office to contact during post-closure care period? _____ _____ _____ _____

   c. Has the post-closure period begun? _____ _____ _____ _____

   d. Is the written post-closure cost estimate available? _____ _____ _____ _____

*Applies only to disposal facilities.

4/82-A

Section I - USE AND MANGEMENT OF CONTAINERS (Part 265, Subpart I)

	YES	NO	NI	Remarks
1. Are containers in good condition?	—	—	—	_____
2. Are containers compatible with waste in them?	—	—	—	_____
3. Are containers managed to prevent leaks?	—	—	—	_____
4. Are containers stored closed?	—	—	—	_____
5. Are containers inspected weekly for leaks and defects.	—	—	—	_____
6. Are ignitable and reactive wastes stored at least 15 meters (50 feet) from the facility property line? (Indicate if waste is ignitable or reactive).	—	—	—	_____
7. Are incompatible wastes stored in separate containers? (If not, the provisions of 40 CFR 265.17(b) apply).	—	—	—	_____
8. Are containers of incompatible waste separated or protected from each other by physical barriers or sufficient distance?	—	—	—	_____

Section J - TANKS (Part 265, Subpart J)

		YES	NO	NI	Remarks

1. Are tanks used to store only those wastes which will not cause corrosion, leakage or premature failure of the tank?

2. Do uncovered tanks have at least 60 cm (2 feet) of free-board, or dikes or other containment structures?

3. Do continuous feed systems have a waste-feed cutoff?

4. Are waste analyses done before the tanks are used to store a substantially different waste than before?

5. Are required daily and weekly inspections done?

6. Are reactive & ignitable wastes in tanks protected or rendered non-reactive or non-ignitable? Indicate if waste is ignitable or reactive. (If waste is rendered non-reactive or non-ignitable, see treatment requirements.)

7. Are incompatible wastes stored in separate tanks? (If not, the provisions of 40 CFR 265.17(b) apply.)

8. Has the owner or operator observed the National Fire Protection Associations buffer zone requirements for tanks containing ignitable or reactive wastes?

   Tank capacity: _____ gallons

   Tank diameter: _____ feet

   Distance of tank from property line _____ feet

   (See table 2 - 1 through 2 - 6 of NFPA's "Flammable and Combustible Liquids Code - 1977" to determine compliance.)

J-1   4/82-A

Appendix GN

Section A: Scope

1.   Complete this Appendix if the owner or operator of a TSD facility also generates
hazardous waste that is subsequently shipped off-site for treatment, storage,
or disposal.

Section B: MANIFEST REQUIREMENTS (Part 262, Subpart B)

		YES	NO	NI	Remarks
(1)	Does the operator have copies of the manifest available for review?	___	___	___	_____
(2)	Examine manifests for shipments in past 6 months. Indicate approximate number of manifested shipments during that period. _____				
(3)	Do the manifest forms examined contain the following information: (If possible, make copies of, or record information from, manifest(s) that do not contain the critical elements).				
a.	Manifest document number?	___	___	___	_____
b.	Name, mailing address, telephone number, and EPA ID number of Generator	___	___	___	_____
c.	Name and EPA ID Number of Transporter(s)?	___	___	___	_____
d.	Name, address, and EPA ID Number Designated permitted facility and alternate facility?	___	___	___	_____
e.	The description of the waste(s) (DOT shipping name, DOT hazard class, DOT identification number)?	___	___	___	_____
f.	The total quantity of waste(s) and the type and number of containers loaded?	___	___	___	_____
g.	Required certification?	___	___	___	_____
h.	Required signatures?	___	___	___	_____

(4)   Reportable exceptions

a.   For manifests examined in (2) (except for shipments within the last 35 days),
enter the number of manifests for which the generator has NOT received a
signed copy from the designated facility within 35 days of the date of shipment. _____

b.   For manifests indicated in (4a), enter the number for which the generator
has submitted exception reports (40 CFR 262.42) to the Regional Administrator. _____

Section C: PRE-TRANSPORT REQUIREMENTS (Part 262, Subpart C)

	YES	NO	NI	Remarks
1. Is waste packaged in accordance with DOT regulations? (Required prior to movement of hazardous waste off-site)	—	—	—	_____
2. Are waste packages marked and labeled in accordance with DOT regulations concerning hazardous waste materials? (Required for movement of hazardous waste off-site)	—	—	—	_____
3. If required, are placards available to transporters of hazardous waste?	—	—	—	_____

4. On-site accumulation of generated hazardous wastes. A HWMF may accumulate hazardous waste it generates either (A) in its storage facility [265.1(b)] or (B) in accordance with 40 CFR 262.34 [see 265.1(c)(7)]. Option B restricts all accumulation to tanks and containers. If the installation elects option A, check this box ⊟ and skip to Section D. If the installation elects option B, complete the following observations:

	YES	NO	NI	Remarks
a. Is each container clearly marked with the start of accumulation date?	—	—	—	_____
b. Have more than 90 days elapsed since the date inspected in (a)?	—	—	—	_____
c. Do wastes remain in accumulation tanks for more than 90 days?	—	—	—	_____
d. Is each container and tank labeled or marked clearly with the words "Hazardous Waste"?	—	—	—	_____

Section D: - RECORDKEEPING AND REPORTING (Part 262, Subpart D)

	YES	NO	NI	Remarks
1. Are all test results and analyses needed for hazardous waste determinations retained for at least three years?	—	—	—	_____

Section E: - INTERNATIONAL SHIPMENTS (Part 262, Subpart E)

	YES	NO	NI	Remarks
1. Has the installation imported or exported Hazardous Waste?	—	—	—	_____

(If answered Yes, complete the following as applicable.)

a. Exporting Hazardous waste; has a generator:

	YES	NO	NI	Remarks
i. Notified the Administrator in writing?	—	—	—	_____
ii. Obtained the signature of the foreign consignee confiming delivery of the waste(s) in the foreign country?	—	—	—	_____
iii. Met the Manifest requirements?	—	—	—	_____
b. Importing Hazardous Waste; has the generator met the manifest requirements?	—	—	—	_____

INSPECTION FORM B

<u>Section A:</u>   Scope of inspection

Standards for generators of HAZARDOUS WASTE subject to 40 CFR 262.10

<u>Section B:</u>   MANIFEST REQUIREMENTS (Part 262, Subpart B)

                                            Yes   No   NI*   Remarks

(1) Does the generator have copies of the manifest
     available for review?   ___   ___ ___   _____

(2) Examine manifests for shipments in past 6
     months. Indicate approximate number of
     manifested shipments during that period. _____

(3) Do the manifest forms examined contain the
     following information? (If possible, make
     copies of, or record information from, manifests
     that do not contain the critical elements)

     a. Manifest document number?   ___   ___ ___   _____

     b. Name, mailing address, telephone number,
         and EPA ID number of generator?   ___   ___ ___   _____

     c. Name and EPA ID number of transporter(s)? ___   ___ ___   _____

     d. Name, Address, and EPA ID Number of designated
         permitted facility and alternate facility? ___   ___ ___   _____

     e. The description of the waste(s) (DOT shipping
         name, DOT hazard class, DOT identification
         number)?   ___   ___ ___   _____

     f. The total quantity of waste(s) and the type
         and number of containers loaded?   ___   ___ ___   _____

     g. Required certification?   ___   ___ ___   _____

     h. Required signatures?   ___   ___ ___   _____

(4) Reportable exceptions

     a. For manifests examined in (2) (except for shipments
         within the last 35 days), enter the number of mani-
         fests for which the generator has <u>NOT</u> received a
         signed copy from the designated facility within 35
         days of the date of shipment. _____

     b. For manifests indicated in (4a), enter the number for
         which the generator has submitted exception reports
         (40 CFR 262.42) to the Regional Administrator. _____

A/B-1   (4-82B)

Section C - PRE-TRANSPORT REQUIREMENTS
(40 CFR Part 262 Subpart C)

		Yes	No	NI	Remarks

(1) Is waste packaged in accordance with DOT regulations? (Required prior to movement of hazardous waste off-site)

(2) Are waste packages marked and labeled in accordance with DOT regulations concerning hazardous waste materials? (Required prior to movement of hazardous waste off-site)

(3) If required, are placards available to transporter?

** (4) Pre-shipment Accumulation:

** applies only to GENERATORS that store hazardous waste on-site for 90 days or less without a permit. These items do not apply to generators whose waste is immediately transported off-site.

a. Is hazardous waste accumulated in containers? If no, skip to b.

  i. Is each container clearly marked with the date on which the period of accumulation began?

  ii. Have more than 90 days elapsed since the dates marked?

  iii. Is each container labeled or marked clearly with the words "Hazardous Wastes?"

  iv. Are containers in good condition?

  v. Are containers compatible with waste in them?

  vi. Are containers managed to prevent leaks?

  vii. Are containers stored closed?

  viii. Are containers inspected weekly for leaks and defects?

  ix. Are ignitable and reactive wastes stored at least 15 meters (50 feet) from the facility property line? (Indicate if waste is ignitable or reactive).

Yes   No   NI   Remarks

   x. Are incompatible wastes stored in
separate containers? (If not, the
provisions of 40 CFR 265.17(b)
apply.)   ___ ___ ___   _____

  xi. Are containers of incompatible waste
separated or protected from each other
by physical barriers or sufficient
distance?   ___ ___ ___   _____

b. Is hazardous waste accumulated in tanks?
If no, skip to c.   ___ ___ ___   _____

   i. Is each tank labeled or marked clearly
with the words "Hazardous Wastes"?   ___ ___ ___   _____

  ii. Are tanks used to store only those
wastes which will not cause corrosion,
leakage or premature failure of the
tank?   ___ ___ ___   _____

 iii. Do uncovered tanks have at least 60 cm
(2 feet) of freeboard, or dikes or other
containment structures?   ___ ___ ___   _____

  iv. Do continuous feed systems have a
waste-feed cutoff?   ___ ___ ___   _____

   v. Are waste analyses done before the tanks
are used to store a substantially different
waste than before?   ___ ___ ___   _____

  vi. Are required daily and weekly inspections
done?   ___ ___ ___   _____

 vii. Are reactive and ignitable wastes in
tanks protected or rendered non-reactive
or nonignitable? Indicate if waste is
ignitable or reactive. (If waste is
rendered non-reactive or nonignitable,
see treatment requirements.)   ___ ___ ___   _____

viii. Are incompatible wastes stored in
separate tanks? (If not, the provisions
of 40 CFR §265.17(b) apply.)   ___ ___ ___   _____

                                       (4-82B)

272   APPENDIX

Yes   No   NI   Remarks

ix. Has the owner or operator observed the National Fire Protection Association's buffer zone requirements for tanks containing ignitable or reactive wastes?

Tank capacity: _____ gallons

Tank diameter: _____ feet

Distance of tank from property line _____ feet

(see tables 2-1 through 2-6 of NFPA's "Flammable and Combustible Liquids Code - 1977" to determine compliance.)

c. Is hazardous waste accumulated in other than tanks or containers?   ___ ___ ___ _____

d. Personnel training.

Do personnel training records include:

i.   Job Titles?   ___ ___ ___ _____

ii. Job Descriptions?   ___ ___ ___ _____

iii. Description of training?   ___ ___ ___ _____

iv. Records of training?   ___ ___ ___ _____

v.   Did personnel receive the required training by 5-19-81?   ___ ___ ___ _____

vi. Do new personnel receive required training within six months?   ___ ___ ___ _____

vii. Do personnel training records indicate that personnel have taken part in an annual review of initial training?   ___ ___ ___ _____

e. Preparedness and Prevention

i. Maintenance and Operation of Facility:

Is there any evidence of fire, explosion, or release of hazardous waste or hazardous waste constituent?   ___ ___ ___ _____

Yes No   NI   Remarks

ii. If required, does this facility
     have the following equipment:

     Internal communications or alarm systems?   ___ ___ ___   _____

     Telephone or 2-way Radios at the scene of
     operations?   ___ ___ ___   _____

     Portable fire extinguishers, fire control,
     spill control equipment and decontamination
     equipment?   ___ ___ ___   _____

        Indicate the volume of water and/or foam available for fire control:

     _____

     _____

iii. Testing and Maintenance of Emergency Equipment:

     Has the owner or operator established
     testing and maintenance procedures
     for emergency equipment?   ___ ___ ___   _____

     Is emergency equipment maintained in
     operable condition?   ___ ___ ___   _____

iv. Has owner/operator provided immediate
     access to internal alarms (if needed)?   ___ ___ ___   _____

v.   Is there adequate aisle space for
     unobstructed movement?   ___ ___ ___   _____

vi. Has the owner or operator attempted to make
     arrangements with local authorities in
     case of an emergency at the facility?   ___ ___ ___   _____

f. Contingency Plan and Emergency Procedures

     Does the contingency plan contain
     the following information:

     i. The actions facility personnel must take
         to comply with §265.51 and 265.56 in response
         to fires, explosions, or any unplanned release
         of hazardous waste? (If the owner has a Spill
         Prevention, Control and Countermeasures (SPCC)
         Plan, he needs only to amend that plan to
         incorporate hazardous waste management
         provisions that are sufficient to comply
         with the requirements of this Part
         (as applicable.)   ___ ___ ___   _____

                    C-4   (4-82B)

Yes No   NI   Remarks

ii. Arrangements agreed to by local police
departments, hospitals, contractors,
and State and local emergency response
teams to coordinate emergency services,
pursuant to §265.37? ___ ___ ___ _____

iii. Names, addresses, and phone numbers (Office
and Home) of all persons qualified to act
as emergency coordinator. ___ ___ ___ _____

iv. A list of all emergency equipment at the
facility which includes the location and
physical description of each item on the
list, and a brief outline of its capabilities? ___ ___ ___ _____

v. An evacuation plan for facility personnel where there is a possibility that
evacuation could be necessary? (This
plan must describe signal(s) to be used
to begin evacuation, evacuation routes
and alternate evacuation routes?) ___ ___ ___ _____

vi. Are copies of the Contingency Plan available
at site and local emergency organizations? ___ ___ ___ _____

vii. Is the facility emergency coordinator
identified? ___ ___ ___ _____

viii. Is coordinator familiar with all aspects of
site operation and emergency procedures? ___ ___ ___ _____

ix. Does the Emergency Coordinator have the
authority to carry out the Contingency
Plan? ___ ___ ___ _____

x. If an emergency situation has occured at
this facility, has the emergency coordinator
followed the emergency procedures listed
in 265.56? ___ ___ ___ _____

(4-82B)

Section D: RECORDKEEPING AND REPORTING (Part 262, Subpart D)

	Yes	No	NI	Remarks

(1) Are all test results and analyses needed for
hazardous waste determinations retained for
at least three years?   ___ ___ ___ _____

Section E: INTERNATIONAL SHIPMENTS (Part 262 Subpart E)

(1) Has the installation imported or exported
hazardous waste? If "no", skip a and b.   ___ ___ ___ _____

   a. Exporting Hazardous Waste, has a generator:

      i. Notified the Administrator in writing?   ___ ___ ___ _____

      ii. Obtained the signature of the foreign
consignee confirming delivery of the
waste(s) in the foreign country?   ___ ___ ___ _____

     iii. Met the Manifest requirements?   ___ ___ ___ _____

   b. Importing Hazardous Waste, has the
generator met the manifest requirements?   ___ ___ ___ _____

Remarks: _____

_____

_____

_____

_____

_____

_____

_____

_____

_____

_____

_____

_____

_____

_____

_____

_____

_____

(4-82B)

Appendix 6

HAZARDOUS WASTE
MANAGEMENT HINTS

1. Use bulk storage/disposal (for large quantities of hazardous waste) whenever feasible. This will (1) save on unit treatment/disposal charges; (2) save on unit transportation charges; and (3) save on drum costs.
2. Use reclaimed drums meeting DOT specifications rather than new drums.
3. Buy process chemicals or other inputs in returnable containers or deposit containers.
4. Send empty drums to a barrel reclaimer.
5. All drum storage should be on pallets to minimize corrosion or deterioration.
6. Do not store drums more than two high.
7. All drum storage should be on concrete pads or similar impermeable base, whenever possible.
8. When dealing with ignitables, ground drums whenever opening the bung, and use nonsparking (brass or plastic) tools.
9. When filling drums or transferring materials or wastes, have absorbent material (cement kiln dust, fly ash, fuller's earth, vermiculite, cementitious materials, oil dry or expanded clay) handy in case of spills. Synthetic absorbent media, often available in "pillows," is especially easy to use.
10. Minimize the transfer of wastes from container to container by accumulating and storing wastes in containers meeting DOT specifications for offsite transportation.
11. Compressed air horns are suitable and inexpensive as the required alarm at a drum storage pad.
12. Properly mark each drum to be used to accumulate each waste. This should be done before the drum is used to accumulate waste materials, as decals and paint will not adhere to a dirty drum. The markings should include "hazardous waste." The date that hazardous wastes were first put in the drum should also be clearly marked. You may wish to put other information on the drum at this time, including any labeling and marking required prior to offsite transportation. If you have had problems in the past with labels fading, peeling or washing off when the drums are moved to outside storage, you may wish to switch label companies or use a duplicate label system (with fresh labels prior to offsite transportation). It is imperative that you be able to identify the con-

tents of each drum in storage. Further, your employees need certain information in order to protect their health and safety, and in order to respond to any spills or fires.

13. Do not allow any empty drums out of company possession before their reclamation by a drum reclaimer or disposal after crushing. Do not allow employees to use empty drums as trash barrels or for any other purposes. This will prevent drums with your firm's markings and another firm's wastes from turning up in unexpected places, such as vacant lots or rural fields.

14. Provide adequate numbers of waste containers for employee use.

15. Separate garbage (waste office paper, boxes, cans, cups, coffee grounds, etc.) from industrial wastes.

16. Obtain material safety data sheets from your vendors for each chemical you use in production, maintenance or housekeeping.

17. Ask vendors for detailed breakdowns (percent by weight or ppm analyses if possible) of all hazardous constituents in the products you purchase. At a minimum, obtain: (1) the closed-cup flashpoint; (2) pH, and (3) some confirmation of the presence or absence of arsenic, barium, cadmium, chromium, lead, mercury, selenium, silver, cyanide and sulfides.

18. Put your vendors to work looking for alternative chemical products that can meet your requirements, without containing (or containing lesser amounts of) hazardous constituents.

19. If you accept any products from a vendor on a trial basis, require as a condition that the vendor take back any unused product or waste resulting from the trial use of his product.

20. Ask your vendor to accept any expired or obsolete or off-specification chemical inputs you have, to send them back to the manufacturer for reformulation.

21. Use training available through vendors, equipment manufacturers, insurance carriers, fire departments, etc. Training presentations or slide shows often can be made available for initial or refresher training. Such training is especially important in the use of personnel safety equipment and dangerous chemicals, and in the use and maintenance of equipment that generates hazardous wastes as a by-product of production.

22. Use the inspection and consultation services available through insurance carriers and fire departments.

23. Minimize the amount of rags needing proper disposal by the use of industrial dry cleaning services. Uniforms, aprons, etc., are also available.

24. Keep chemical baths (such as caustic stripping solutions or solvent cleaning solutions) covered when not in use. This will minimize evaporation and contamination. Keep containers closed.

25. Avoid off-specification charges (for free liquids) at the landfill by filling the last portion of the disposal container with a suitable amount of absorbent material. This is especially important for sludges or nonsolid materials containing easily separated liquids. The vibration resulting from transportation will cause a layer of liquid to form on the top of such materials, resulting in an off-specification disposal charge unless some absorbent is present. Check with your disposal site.

26. Explore incineration or chemical treatment for liquid waste streams not amenable to biological treatment.

27. Explore biological treatment for liquid waste streams via the municipal sewage treatment plant.
28. Visit any disposal facility (or treatment facility) prior to shipping any waste there.
29. Require the treatment or disposal facility to show you copies of their federal and state permits. Require such facilities to show proof of insurance. Check such facilities with the state and with their insurance carrier.
30. Call your state hazardous waste management officials with any questions you have.
31. Do not use onsite surface impoundments or landfills for hazardous wastes.
32. If you do not already know, find out where your wastes are going.
33. Use price and service competition between different commercial firms in the hazardous waste management business. Services that may be available include (1) pickups every 90 days (or 30 days for small-quantity generators); (2) partial load pickups (a full semi-trailer holds ~80 drums); (3) brokering of wastes to other hazardous waste management firms (i.e., "one-stop" disposal); and (4) free consulting/training. However, do not be "penny-wise and pound-foolish." There are still plenty of firms that operate in violation of the law, or that make use of "grey areas." Remember, you and your company are responsible for the hazardous wastes generated by your activities. If you pay to have them recycled or brokered to disposal and the broker goes bankrupt, then you will have to pay again for proper disposal. The second time around will be under the close scrutiny of the state board of health, department of natural resources and environmental protection agency.
34. Explore recycling options. Do cost/benefit calculations for both onsite processing and offsite recycling.
35. Attempt to use a waste exchange.
36. Use the waste management hierarchy.
37. Use recoverable solvents, coolants, oils, hydraulic fluids, etc.
38. If you can arrange it, let your vendor "store" your hazardous material (chemical) inventory for you by purchasing the minimum amounts necessary. Find a vendor with short delivery time, so as to minimize inventory.
39. Keep ignitable wastes out of direct sunlight and out of black barrels.
40. Obtain a copy of insurance certificate [required by the U.S. Department of Transportation (DOT)] from transporters.
41. Always have an alternate treatment facility or disposal site lined up. This is especially important if you accumulate for 90 days under 262.34.
42. Use nonreturnable product drums for disposal. Do not put wastes in deposit or returnable drums that the related raw material came in. However, make sure the waste is compatible with any residue in an "empty" drum, especially if the drum used formerly contained an unrelated product. Make sure the type of drum used meets DOT specifications for the type of material put in it.
43. Allow space for expansion when filling drums with solvents or other volatile liquids.
44. Do not expect commercial treatment or disposal firms to return the drums the waste was shipped in.

45. Accumulate wastes in truckload quantities (~75 drums), if possible, to minimize transportation costs per unit (weight or volume).
46. Get material safety data sheets for all chemicals used at the manufacturing firm. Find out the shelf life of all such chemicals. Rotate inventory to avoid obsolete or expired products needing disposal.
47. Leaky or weak drums should never be shipped or stored. The contents of such containers should immediately be transferred to another drum, or the drum itself (contents and container) should be placed inside a larger container, known as an overpack drum.
48. Waste-to-waste compatibility should be considered in designating areas within an overall storage area where each waste type is to be placed.
49. The generator should ascertain whether a commercial hazardous waste management facility under consideration has the capability to handle a particular waste stream in the specified manner. Site capabilities vary widely, and at present the mere fact that a commercial facility is a treatment, storage or disposal (TSD) facility does not imply much. Obtaining recognition from the U.S. Environmental Protection Agency (EPA) as a TSD facility means only that the facility was "in existence" on November 19, 1980, and filed a notification of hazardous waste activity and a permit application by the deadline dates. Such a facility need only have the capability of storing hazardous wastes. No assumptions can be made regarding the quality of a commercial facility, the facility's capabilities or their compliance status.
50. Develop and maintain good relationships with competent transportation and disposal firms.
51. Develop and maintain good relationships with officials in state regulatory agencies.
52. Be cautious in dealing with commercial hazardous waste management firms (waste brokers) that accept wastes for storage, and then arrange to have other firms treat or dispose of the wastes. If the services of a waste broker are used, find out the final disposition of each waste so managed, and obtain a certificate of disposal from the ultimate treatment or disposal site.
53. Expect to have to use the services of different commercial hazardous waste management firms for different types of waste streams. Different types of wastes will often require different treatment or disposal methods, or differing sequences of methods. It is unlikely that one hazardous waste management firm can perform all the necessary hazardous waste management methods at one site for all of the waste streams found at a manufacturing facility.
54. Price is not the only factor to consider when dealing with commercial hazardous waste management firms. The quality of the facility, the competence of employees, the services provided and the firm's reputation should also be taken into account.
55. Do not deal with transporters or commercial hazardous waste management firms whose representatives do not exhibit a firm grasp of the regulations and of hazardous waste management in general.
56. Do not deal with transporters or commercial hazardous waste management firms that seem to operate at the borderline of legality, or who accept any waste without written documentation of the waste's identity

or properties. Responsible firms will require a great deal of information about the waste and the process generating it prior to accepting the waste for treatment/disposal.

57. Do not try to ship wastes to a treatment or disposal site without approval from the site. In many states, the approval of the state regulatory agency is also required.

58. Do not try to "sneak" wastes that have been rejected as unsuitable for land disposal into a hazardous waste disposal site. The regulations require the inspection of all incoming shipments and verification that the wastes shipped match the description provided on the manifest. Many sites perform what are known as "fingerprint" analyses on incoming wastes, before acceptance. A generator will be sorry if the disposal operator discovers a "ringer" and even sorrier when the wastes are returned at the generator's cost. The generator may become a former customer of the site as a result, and enforcement actions can also be an outcome of such behavior.

59. Segregate hazardous waste streams and immediately identify the contents of any container used for accumulating wastes.

60. In most situations, mixing hazardous wastes with nonhazardous wastes is not a suitable method of managing or treating or disposing of such materials. In general, hazardous wastes should be separated from other wastes and managed with all due care.

61. Do not try to sneak hazardous wastes (even in small quantities) into a sanitary (municipal waste) landfill. The generator will be sorry if such wastes are discovered "hidden" among the garbage and refuse from the plant. The generator will be even sorrier if such wastes catch fire or explode as a hot bulldozer runs over the wastes to compact them. Enforcement action may also result from such behavior.

62. Wherever possible switch from drum disposal to bulk disposal.

63. Follow the flow of each of your virgin materials to determine where it becomes a waste. Then determine if there are any ways to recover the material for in-plant use. If not, try to determine if the material has a potential for reuse by other industries (waste exchanges).

64. Inspect the facilities your company uses on a regular basis to determine that the wastes your company sent them have actually been processed and that the flow pattern through the facility has been observed (check their operating records).

65. Make certain that the TSD your company is using has the proper environmental impairment liability insurance for the state in which they are operating, and request a certificate of insurance for your files.

66. Check with the state regulatory agency on any facilities you intend to use. They have files on all licensed facilities, which are public information.

67. Approach landfilling waste streams as a temporary solution to disposal of your waste streams. Landfills should be viewed as nothing more than long-term storage.

68. Inspect offsite laboratories before choosing one to perform your analyses; consider the methods that they will use to perform the analyses and the types of equipment which will be used.

69. Organize all of your Resource Conservation and Recovery Act (RCRA)

files in a centralized location. Maintain copies of all of your material safety data sheets next to your contingency plan so that immediate access is available to all emergency response personnel.

70. Maintain a site map at different locations in the plant along with copies of the contingency plan. This site map should include gas shutoffs, electricity shutoffs, emergency exits, evacuation rendezvous locations and emergency first aid equipment locations throughout the plant. Also locate special hazard areas throughout the plant. This map, when used in conjunction with your contingency plan, will allow emergency response units to properly and effectively respond to any emergencies.

71. Maintain accident/injury forms on all employees and make certain the local hospital is familiar with their use. The form includes information that is normally given by the victim if he is conscious. This information includes the person's name, next of kin, family physician's name, phone numbers, type of injury, first aid performed on the injured party, type of exposure, medical history of the injured party (including allergies to antibiotics, blood type, contact lenses being worn, types of medication the injured party is currently taking, diseases or ailments the injured party is known to suffer from, and the date of the last tetanus toxoid booster).

72. In putting together a training program, consider free training provided by local emergency organizations, such as the local fire department or the Red Cross, your insurance companies, materials vendors, etc.

73. Monitor your plant effluent to determine whether you are losing precious chemicals. Learn to use your effluent as a gauge on your material efficiencies.

74. Maintain a good rapport with state regulatory officials; they can be very helpful in solving your hazardous waste problems.

75. Try to attend information seminars which deal specifically with your state's regulatory programs. This will access you to specific state regulations and allow you to meet people who share your compliance problems and who may have already solved some of these problems.

76. Make certain that your company attorneys are up-to-date on RCRA and Superfund regulations.

77. When dealing with hazardous waste disposal, document everything. This includes company contacts, facility contacts, transporter contacts, waste analyses and waste manifests.

78. Make certain that all employees who will be handling hazardous wastes are properly trained and have been given job-specific instructions on safety as well as job duties. Also, make certain that when a person is working with hazardous waste, immediate communication or a spotter is available to determine the well-being of the individual.

79. Managing hazardous wastes is best accomplished by assigning the duty to one person who will stand as the RCRA authority for the plant. Committee work is not feasible.

80. The 90-day accumulators should be sure to allow some lag time for the inevitable delays associated with getting approval from the state and the disposal site for wastes previously managed at other sites.

81. The 90-day accumulators may want to make preliminary arrangements

with a second disposal site. This site would be used if the primary site would be unable to accept wastes for some reason.

82. Use an internal labeling system.

83. Examine all process chemicals used and chemical outputs and intermediates for appearance on the 261.33(e)-(f) lists.

84. Plug drains in storage areas.

85. Do not let employees use empty product or waste drums for burn barrels.

86. Use simple treatment methods not requiring a permit, such as solidification, whenever possible.

87. Institute internal reporting/recordkeeping systems to be able to generate information for the annual report on a quarterly basis.

88. Read the regulations yourself. Take your time. It is much cheaper than having a consultant read them for you. If you have any questions, call your state regulatory agency. If you need an interpretation of how the regulations apply to a particular situation, ask for one. Certain interpretations should be in writing, especially those dealing with the applicable regulatory category.

89. You may wish to purchase a commercial "spill kit" or make one of your own with an open head drum, absorbent, gloves, respirator, shovels, etc.

90. Get it in writing.

91. Disgruntled employees and ex-employees will tell all. If certain activities are "shady," do not do them, because sooner or later your employees or their friends or relatives will turn the company in. Do not ask employees to do anything you would not want regulatory officials to know about.

92. Obtain copies of all offsite facility's and transporter's permits. Familiarize yourself with any agreements that the facility or transporter have with the regulatory authorities.

93. Use the RCRA/Superfund Hazardous Waste Hotline (1-800-424-9346 or 1-202-382-3000) to get answers to questions or to order information materials.

94. Use the Chemtrec hotline (1-800-424-9300) for information when there is a transportation-related incident involving hazardous materials.

INDEX